Horst & Gisela
Wolfgang

Orchids
Crete & Dodecanese

The orchid flora of the islands of Crete,
Kasos, Karpathos and Rhodes

MEDITERRANEO EDITIONS

2004

Orchids
Crete & Dodecanese

The orchid flora of the islands of Crete,
Kasos, Karpathos and Rhodes

HORST & GISELA KRETZSCHMAR
WOLFGANG ECCARIUS

TRANSLATION
JILL PITTINGER

ART EDITOR
VANGELIS PAPIOMITOGLOU

Published by
MEDITERRANEO EDITIONS
36 Govatzidaki str. 74100 Rethymno Crete Greece
Tel. +30 28310 21590, Fax +30 28310 21591
e-mail: stella@mediterraneo.gr
www.mediterraneo.gr

Authors
Dr. Horst & Gisela Kretzschmar, Goethestr. 4c, D-36251 Bad Hersfeld
Prof. Dr. Wolfgang Eccarius, Amrastr. 107, D-999817 Eisenach

ISBN: 960-8227-42-9

CONTENTS

Introduction

With the previous publications of the detailed guides, Orchideen auf Rhodos (KRETZSCHMAR et al, 2001) and Orchideen auf Kreta, Kasos und Kaparthos (KRETZSCHMAR et al, 2002) the authors presented the results of twenty years of research in the field. Since then, a wish has often been expressed to us for the publication of a compact softback edition which would be useful as a "field-guide", covering the whole of the southern island chain of the Aegean. An opportunity presented itself through an offer to publish such a little book from Editions Mediterraneo.

It is naturally impossible to reproduce the fine-resolution cartography included in the books mentioned above in such a limited space; however, a distribution is put forward for every variety on the basis of UTM 10 kilo-metre-fields, divided into two time zones (pre- and post 1980). The concept of species, with sensible and easily understandable division into the main species and sub-species found in the region, is retained. Taxa which have subsequently been newly-described in the range of species have not been included because, according to the views held here they only represent local variations which have arisen as a result of particular ecological conditions, and only constitute a temporary phenomenon. In all, 70 species with 23 sub-species are dealt with here, while 5 further species are to be viewed as questionable or instable.

New, impressive hybrids were found on further visits to the islands and many new photographs were taken which have been included within this book. Our endeavour to show the breadth of variation of the species has been retained, in spite of the lack of space. Our judgment that a number of considerably conspicuous deviations can unreservedly be classified within the variations of the main genera, stems from the knowledge that a high degree of variability exists within many species. The fortunate outcome of this, results in the particularly rich illustration of this book through more than 500 photographs. Both the date and the location at which it was taken is given for every photograph; the photographer is named in the case of the small number of photographs which did not originate from the authors of the book. In addition, the island in question is referred to by an abbreviation in brackets (CR for Crete, KP for Karpathos, KA for Kasos, and RH for Rhodes).

The introductory chapter presents a short overview of the geographical and geological data concerning the area. It is followed by a brief excursion into the other flora and the fauna. It ends with a cartographical presentation of the distribution of species for the four islands, as well as a description of the situation regarding particularly endangered species and some special environments. A detailed discussion of the taxonomic problems has pur-posely been omitted, and only an overview of all Taxa in the sequence in which they appear in the list of species has been included.

The main part of this field-guide naturally comprises a discussion of the species. A number of the orchid species belong within categories which present especial difficulty, since they have a particularly high tendency towards hybridisation. In order to facilitate familiarisation and their identification for the user of this book, these species are summarised according to the respective "relationship-group" named after a main species (Groups: *Ophrys mammosa-sphegodes*, *Ophrys episcopalis-oestrifera*, *Ophrys fusca* and *Orchis anatolica*). This term does not represent a taxonomic ranking, but is simply to be understood as a didactic expedient.

The species are listed alphabetically in the catalogue of species, according to their scientific names. The groups are listed according to group names in this sequence and within a group the species belonging to it appear once more in alphabetical order. In addition, endemic species, see above (this applies only to Crete) are indicated when the name of a species or subspecies appears in red. Instable species, which only appear as single, chance finds and species whose finding has not been confirmed to date, are briefly described in the appendix to the section on species.

Every species is presented with detailed diagnostics and it's preferred habitats are described. In the case of each species, hybrids found in the area are listed. Possible points of confusion with other species are noted, as well as possible delimitations between them. The presentation of each species concludes with a note on the flowering period and an overview of its distribution.

Hybrids follow the species in alphabetical order according to their hybrid formula. In all, 86 different hybrids are presented.

The final part contains a description of a number of recommended excursions, to enable every user of the book to delve rapidly into the fascinating area of the orchids of the southern Aegean. The list of literature cited in the book is followed by some notes on the photographic methods employed and a list comprising all the Taxa dealt with in the book, as well as their page references.

The islands of the Dodecanese and Crete

The Greek islands of Crete, Kasos and Karpathos are situated together with numerous small islands in the Mediterranean, south-east of the Peloponnese; Kasos and Karpathos belong to the so-called Dodecanese. The latter two islands lie at distances of around 52 and 76 kms respectively, east-north-east of Crete.

Crete is the largest of the Greek islands and the fifth largest island in the Mediterranean (after Sicily, Sardinia, Cyprus and Corsica); it extends in a west-east orientation and has an area of around 8,700 sq. kms, with a length of around 250 kms. Its greatest width is 56 kms, and its narrowest (to the east of Ierapetra) only 12 kms.

Four mountain massifs, separated from one another, lie along its lengthwise axis. They are the Lefka Ori in the west (reaching to 2452 m), the Ida massif (Psiloritis) in the middle of the island (reaching to 2456 m), the Dikti massif in the eastern part of central Crete (with peaks rising to almost 2150 m) and the Sitia mountains (reaching to 1476 m) in eastern Crete. In addition to the latter there are many other mountain ridges which often reach heights in excess of 1000 m. Large areas of plain are not found on Crete with the exception of the low-lying Mesara Plain in south-central Crete, which is almost 50 kms in length but only a few kilometres in width. Of the numerous streams and rivers, which are usually only short in extent and do not always contain water, the most important are the Yioferos, which flows into the sea on the north coast, and the Yeropotamos and Anapodaris,

Ayios Ioannis (CR), view towards Psiloritis, 3.4.94

which have their mouths on the south coast.

A notable morphological characteristic of Crete is the existence of high-lying, undrained basins; the largest of these is the Lasithi High Plateau.

The north coast of Crete is well-punctuated by bays and peninsulas. Mountainous massifs alternate with little coastal plains; almost all of the cities of Crete are located there. The south coast, which for the most part falls away steeply into the sea, is by contrast much more sparsely inhabited.

Geologically, the island is the largest remnant of a continuous fault massif, which was created during the alpine orogenetic phase of the Oligocene (more than 30 million years ago) and which connected the Peloponnese with the mountains of south-west Anatolia in a wide arc.

The rock formations of Crete comprise deposits of the Quaternary, Neogene (Miocene to Pliocene), and pre-Neogene layers (recent Palaeozoic to old Tertiary). The latter are divided into the basal series (about 300 million years old) with two series which have pushed over them, the Tripolitsa and Ethia series.

On the surface there are frequent outcrops of carbonate-rich rocks (limestone to dolomite), which are subject to strong karstic weathering and erosion; this is eloquently witnessed by the existence of over 3,000 caves and numerous canyon-like gorges, of which the Samaria Gorge is the most famous. In lowland areas, this erosion results in the widely-distributed red earth, which in the mountains is replaced in certain locations by yellowish clays. There, the soils have been largely washed away and the ground is reduced to its bedrock. The flysch also often contains components that are basic in reaction.

The schists in particular give an acid reaction, and their erosion produces a yellowish-red, quartz and humus-rich soil. The primarily basic soils of the poljas, through the leaching-out process, may also exhibit a weak to moder-

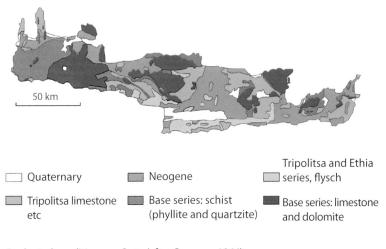

50 km

		Tripolitsa and Ethia
☐ Quaternary	▦ Neogene	▦ series, flysch
▦ Tripolitsa limestone etc	▦ Base series: schist (phyllite and quartzite)	▮ Base series: limestone and dolomite

Geological conditions on Crete (after CREUTZBURG 1966)

ate acid reaction. This variety of soils partly explains the great richness of variety of the Cretan orchid flora.

The climatic conditions on Crete are due on the one hand to its position in the Mediterranean area and on the other to the strongly mountainous nature of the island. Most of the precipitation, increasing from bottom to top and from east to west, falls in the months of November to March, often in the mountains as snow which can last in the peaks into early summer. Above all, the millennia of influence which human activity has had on Crete have left their stamp on the present-day vegetational cover of the island. It's aspect is characterised to a very small extent by cultivated land (olive groves, citrus plantations) but more often by the various stages of degradation of the evergreen forests.

Forests, which make up only about 2% of the surface area, mainly consist of *Acer sempervirens, Ceratonia siliqua, Cupressus sempervirens, Pistacia lentiscus, Quercus coccifera* and *Q. ilex*) and are mostly in the thin, pre-forest and bush-forest-woodland stage of development because of forest grazing, burning and coppicing. In some places, as everywhere else in the Mediterranean region, they have been replaced, mostly by secondary pine forests (*Pinus brutia* intermixed with *Cupressus sempervirens*). The forests in the gorges of Crete are only of small extent but they are important where the existence of some of the species of orchid are concerned.

On the other hand, phrygana, a combination of evergreen shrubs and bushes with a plethora of half-sized and dwarf bushes is widely distributed, being protected against animal grazing by thorns and prickles, essential oils or toxic substances. It owes its existence above all to the extensive grazing

Tulipa doerfleri on fallow land near Yerakari (CR), 12.04.01

Mountain phrygana on Afendis Kavousi, with a view towards the village of Thripti (CR), 9.5.97

practices which have been carried on since antiquity. If in addition to the typical dwarf bushes the phrygana contains potential forest trees that are at the bush stage but which as a result of the discontinuation of grazing over the course of time progress into the pre-forest stage, then the term garigue is applicable.

Finally but not to be forgotten, there are the extensively cultivated fields of grain, fallow land, abandoned arable land and olive groves; here a floral pageant frequently delights the eye, thanks to the presence of *Gladiolus italicus, Anemone coronaria* or *Tulipa doerfleri* and many other species.

Kasos, with It's area of only 66 sq kms (19 kms in length and 6.6 kms wide) is the smallest of the islands dealt with here, while Karpathos, extending in a north-south direction (with a length of nearly 50 kms and a greatest width of 15 kms) and together with the island of Saria which is separated from it by a narrow channel, has an area of around 305 sq kms. Karpathos is broken up into three mountain massifs, the result of recently-formed *Graben* (faults): the Homali massif in the south, the Kalilimni massif (1213 m) in the central section, and a narrow massif in the north which continues on the island of Saria. As a result of numerous disturbances, the whole island has been broken up into a mosaic of soils. The highest point on Kasos is Prionos, in the east of the island, at 601 m.

Both islands are marked by a dearth of flatlands; where these exist, they are of extremely small extent. Modest arable cultivation is only possible on artificially laid-out terraces.

From a geological standpoint, the rocks which are dominant on both islands are of the basic type. Kasos consists almost exclusively of marbles of the limestone series containing hornstone. The mountain massifs of Karpathos were formed from solid limestone sequences of the Jura to the Eocene; flysch, gypsum, calcareous limestone and limestone breccia are also widespread. Here too, assisted by deforestation, the soils are either washed away or down to the barest remnants. Barren rock can be seen over a wide area, fissured through erosion.

By contrast, the area of forest on Karpathos when compared to that of Crete is considerably larger. The forests on Karpathos are usually of the secondary pine forest type, or remains of pine forests.

The dominant assemblage of plants on both Kasos and Karpathos is that of phrygana. On the steeper slopes it is mostly quite sparse; it is only thick on the slopes with a gentler gradient. The latter is mostly the case in the southern part of Karpathos.

The broad areas of erosion landscape in the north of Karpathos are mainly attributable to the geological characteristics of the very loose flysch to be found there, which together with the acid subsoil, so extremely poor in nutrients, only permits a minimal vegetational cover which is lacking in variety of species.

Countless abandoned terraces are notable on Kasos; these bear witness to an earlier, much larger population on the island; in antiquity it is said to have consisted of over 15,000 inhabitants.

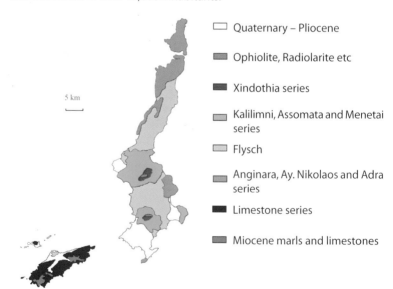

5 km

Quaternary – Pliocene

Ophiolite, Radiolarite etc

Xindothia series

Kalilimni, Assomata and Menetai series

Flysch

Anginara, Ay. Nikolaos and Adra series

Limestone series

Miocene marls and limestones

Geological structure:
Karpathos (after JACOBSHAGEN 1986) and Kasos (IGME 1984)

Ferula communis growing on abandoned agricultural land at Katodio (KP), 1.4.98

Mouth of a valley formed by erosion at Forokli (KP), northern Karpathos, 27.03.01

Abandoned settlement of Skafi in a high valley on Kasos, 22.3.01

The island of Rhodes, situated in the southern Aegean, is about 78 kms in length and 35 kms in breadth at its widest part. It is the largest island of the Dodecanese and the fourth largest of all the Greek islands, with an area of 1,300 sq kms.

From its outward appearance, Rhodes is an island of contrasts. The northern part is given over to tourism; along the west coast, the area of tourism extends from Rhodes City to Kremasti and on the eastern coast to Faliraki. There are also some smaller tourist centres in the west as far as Kalavarda and in the east, as far as Lindos in the south.

By contrast, the southern part and in particular the interior of the island have to a considerable degree, remained untouched by tourism. The most attractive areas in the whole landscape are to be found here.

From the point of view of climate, Rhodes does full justice to its designation as an "island of light", since on average it enjoys more than 3,000 hours of sunshine per year! Rain falls mostly during the frost-free winter, while the summers are very hot and extremely dry.

The terrain of Rhodes can for the most part be categorised as hilly. Greater height is only reached in small areas by Attaviros (1215 m), Akramitis (825 m), and Profitis Ilias (798 m). Larger rivers which are continually fed are relatively rare; the longest is Gaidouras (23 kms) which rises on Profitis Ilias and follows a very winding course to its mouth north of Kalathos.

The geology of Rhodes is extremely complex due to the complicated geological history of the Aegean. The island is situated in an area which is seismically active, as is demonstrated by the numerous earthquakes which have struck into recent times; thus numerous rifts/faults (Graben) can be seen on the geological map. The surface is otherwise mostly characterised by Tertiary (Cenozoic) and Triassic (Mesozoic) sediments, many consisting of chalks or dolomite. As a rule, the Tertiary flysch on Rhodes (flysch = "gently flowing") also contains basic-reacting components. Neutral or acid rocks (e.g. sandstone) are found to a much smaller extent, thus meeting the very varying requirements of the individual varieties of orchids where the

The upper course of the Gaidouras (RH), 10.4.95

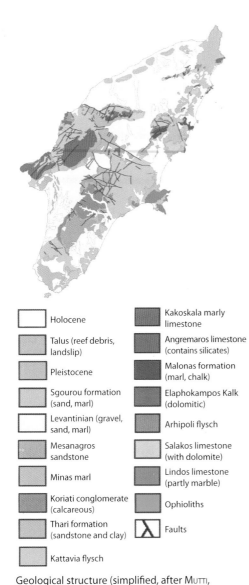

Holocene

Talus (reef debris, landslip)

Pleistocene

Sgourou formation (sand, marl)

Levantinian (gravel, sand, marl)

Mesanagros sandstone

Minas marl

Koriati conglomerate (calcareous)

Thari formation (sandstone and clay)

Kattavia flysch

Kakoskala marly limestone

Angremaros limestone (contains silicates)

Malonas formation (marl, chalk)

Elaphokampos Kalk (dolomitic)

Arhipoli flysch

Salakos limestone (with dolomite)

Lindos limestone (partly marble)

Ophioliths

Faults

Geological structure (simplified, after MUTTI, OROMBELLI & POZZI, 1960-65)

chemistry of the soil is concerned. The large number of species from this plant family can at least partly be explained by the existence of advantageous geological conditions.

With regard to the distribution of the orchids, Rhodes has an advantage in that it offers many and varied biotopes. Among the most important of these is the forest biotope, which is relatively frequently found on Rhodes when compared to other Greek islands. It is probable that sclerophyllous forest with sporadic occurrences of *Pinus brutia* was originally dominant, but it suffered great decimation during antiquity in order to provide timber for shipbuilding. During the period of Italian occupation in the first half of the 20th century, the reforestation of large areas with non-indigenous Aleppo pine (*Pinus halepensis*) was undertaken. Unfortunately these trees are susceptible to forest fires and pest attack; during the eighties of the 20th century large areas of this reforestation were largely destroyed by such fires.

In the course of natural succession, first to develop on the areas of forest which have been cut or burned down is phrygana, a heathland of dwarf scrub. If grazing there is not too severe, it gradually becomes bushland comprising sclerophyllous thickets of 2 or 3 metres in height.

The Plant and Animal World: General Information

The flora of the islands, dealt with in this book, is very rich in variety. According to figures published in JAHN & SCHÖNFELDER (1995) there are around 1,900 species of green leaf and flowering plants on Crete alone, while the corresponding number on Karpathos and Kasos is about 950.

The number of endemic species is especially high – 9.4% on Crete; most of the latter are probably to be viewed as the remainder of once more widely-distributed, weakly competitive genera, which have been able to survive due to long isolation afforded by the insular identity of Crete, while in other places they have long been replaced by more strongly competitive varieties.

Almost half of all the species are annual plants; this is an especially characteristic feature of the Mediterrranean climate. In particular a large number of them are geophytes, among which most of the representatives of the orchid flora belong. By contrast, the area is relatively poor in tall-growing species of bush and tree; water plants only play a quite marginal role. While the three westerly islands have more in common with Europe in their plant population, the flora of Rhodes tends more towards that of Asia Minor. There too, 29 endemic species are to be found; the few pictures here should give an impression of the treasures among them.

Birds of prey can often be observed on Crete; they find ideal nesting places in the high rocky walls of the numerous, highly inaccessible gorges. In addition to various species of eagle and falcon, griffon vultures can often be seen circling high in the sky on the lookout for grazing animals that have met their demise.

The most well-known of the fauna of Rhodes is the Spotted Harlequin butterfly (*Callimorpha quadripunctata*), which makes its appearance in great masses in the Valley of the Butterflies at Petaloudes.

Fritillaria rhodia
Kattavia (RH), 6.4.95

Paeonia clusii ssp. rhodia, Messanagros
(RH), 19.3.03

Every year huge numbers of people come to the narrow valley from July to September, to marvel at the swarms of butterflies attracted by the strongly-scented resin of the amber tree (*Liquidambar orientalis*), which is widely distributed in the valley.

Gynandriris monophylla, Kato Saktouria (CR), 13.4.94

Giant emerald lizard (*Lacerta trilineata*), Epta Piges (RH), 10.4.83

Tulipa bakeri, Yerakari (CR), 6.4.94

Tulipa cretica, Vatos (CR), 5.4.94

The Distribution of and threat to, the Orchids

The island of Rhodes, in comparison to the other regions of the Aegean, underwent development for tourism at a very early date. Thus, as a result of various visits there, it was possible to publish the first maps showing the distribution of the orchids as early as 1981 (KALTEISEN & WILLING) and 1984 (KRETZSCHMAR, WENKER & WILLING). The area studied, in particular Crete and Rhodes, is one of the most orchid-rich regions of Europe, both where the density of species and the individual number of occurrences of some species are concerned. Especially informative are the maps showing the density of species' distribution (see right: because of the limitations of space the much more northerly-situated island of Rhodes is shown separately). Within a 10 kilometre framework there are 20 fields with 40 or more Taxa on Crete and Rhodes together! This profusion of species is a result of the very strong diversity, over a small area, of the landscape and its usage.

The presentation of the distribution for all of the islands is based on over 36,000 individual finds. A considerable number of these were recorded since 1982 by the authors themselves. The fact that the data put together by RALF JAHN within the framework of his studies of this area, could be incorporated into the mapping, proved to be of particular advantage. This data has been included in two of our earlier books (KRETZSCHMAR et al., 2001 and 2002). In spite of the great profusion of species, numerous species of orchids and their biotopes are threatened by various factors in this area. Among these are:

Density of occurrence of species: number of Taxa observed in the 10 km frame. Squares which are highlighted in a dark colour are particularly rich in species.

1. Building operations, and thus a complete loss of growing habitat; this is especially true in the case of wet biotopes near the coast. The boom in hotel construction has led to the destruction of nearly all coastal marshes. The northern tip

of Rhodes affords one of the saddest examples of how the growth of tourism affects nature.

2. Grazing of phrygana, which is often excessive. Both over-grazing and even more lack of pasturing are extremely detrimental to this type of landscape. Itinerant grazing (Goats and sheep) is seldom carried out now-a-days, instead such animals are put into enclosures (especially on Crete), which results in localised, extreme over-grazing. In other places the phrygana vegetation grows progressively taller and impenetrable, with the result that plants which particularly require light find less and less space.

3. The harnessing of natural springs in the higher regions, to supply crops grown on lower lying fields, leads to the drying of the forested gorges and similar places.

4. Forest fires in the latter regions have led, particularly in south-eastern Crete, but even more so on Rhodes, to the loss of a great area of pine forests. While this benefits species which require light, it reduces the milieu available to actual forest species.

The most widely-distributed species are *Anacamptis pyramidalis, Ophrys phryganae* and *Ophrys sicula* on the 3 westerly islands, and *Ophrys sicula, Ophrys speculum* and *Ophrys regis-ferdinandii* on Rhodes, where a range of further species has a markedly regional distribution, for example because of a connection with a particular biotope. One may find that quite large populations of *Ophrys dodekanensis, Orchis laxiflora, Orchis provincialis* or *Serapias orientalis* may occur locally.

Alongside most of the endemic species, *Ophrys fleischmannii, Orchis tridentata, Dactylorhiza romana, Ophrys sitiaca* (on Crete) and *Spiranthes spiralis* are rare, although the latter may often have been overlooked. Only a few of the squares on the grid are inhabited by *Epipactis microphylla, Himantoglossum samariense, Listera ovata, Orchis provincialis, Cephalanthera longifolia* and *Orchis palustris*. Direct protective measures should be demanded where their biotope is concerned, in order to maintain their number. This also applies to all endemic species and subspecies which are distributed in mountainous areas; of these most only have a sporadic distribution.

A final group is that of the species which have only gained a foothold in individual examples or in very small populations (instable occurrence). Among these are *Ophrys speculum* and *Ophrys melena* on Crete, *Ophrys umbilicata* ssp. *rhodia* and *Orchis morio* ssp. *picta* on Karpathos. The instance of *Cephalanthera rubra* and *Epipogium aphyllum* on Crete is quite doubtful.

Comperia comperiana, Cephalanthera epipactoides, Cephalanthera longifolia and *Orchis punctulata* on Rhodes are not counted here among the instable species, because there is a definite occurrence of them on the Turkish mainland only a few kilometres away and new colonisations are to be expected.

Aceras anthropophorum (L.) W.T.Aiton
Man Orchid

Diagnostics: the only species of the orchis relationship without a spur. Small, hanging flowers with a lip divided into four thread-like lobes, arranged in slim spikes. The colour of the lip and the helmet formed by the other petals, varies considerably from light yellow to dark red. Basal rosette of leaves, unspotted. Mostly delicate plants, rarely more than 30 cms high.

Habitat: in meadowy phrygana, also in thin pine woodland, reliant on calcareous subsoil. Mostly as single plants in open spaces; sometimes however also in large populations. Most instances on Rhodes are in the area of Profitis Ilias.

Flowering period: beginning to end of IV

Hybrids: evidenced on Crete and Karpathos, with *Orchis italica* and *Orchis simia*.

Vatos (CR), 11.4.2001

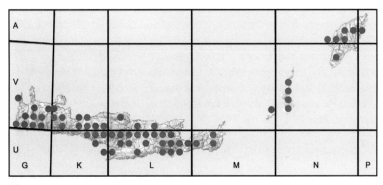

Yerakari (CR), 11.4.2001

Aperi (KP), 25.3.2001

Ayios Isidoros (RH), 7.4.95

19

Anacamptis pyramidalis (L.) Rɪᴄʜ.
Pyramidal Orchid

Diagnostics: tall, slim plant, the narrow leaves of the basal rosette are often already withered at time of flowering. Colour of the flowers pinkish-red to white, three-lobed lip, with two conspicuous bosses between which a longer, thread-like spur projects. Flowers arranged in pointed, cone-shaped inflorescence, hence the name.

Habitat: phrygana, in open spaces, ruderal places, not a demanding plant, found on basic subsoil up to a height of 1500 metres. Common on all islands.

Hybrids: On Rhodes, with *Orchis fragrans.*

Flowering period: end of III to end of IV

Confusion: it's slim appearance is very characteristic; the flowers are unmistakable due to the length of the spur and the presence of the two bosses. The basal leaf rosette is often difficult to distinguish from that of *Orchis fragrans.*

Kattavia (RH), 28.3.02

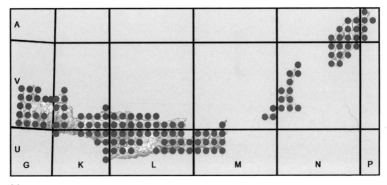

Goudouras (CR), 10.4.94

Ayios Isidoros (RH), 12.5.97

Ay. Ioannis (CR), 22.5.01

Makris Yialos (KP), 30.3.98

21

Barlia robertiana (Loisel.) Greuter
Robert's giant orchid

Diagnostics: large, strong leaves enclose the stems of this substantial plant (often as thick as a finger) like a sheath. In full bloom, strong specimens reach a height of over 50 cms. The flowers are large and arranged in a dense spike, and the lip is 3-lobed with the tip of the middle lobe divided up again. Colour of the flowers is very variable, from white to intense, dark violet, and they are strongly fragrant. The plant is close to the genera *Himantoglossum* and *Comperia*, but in contrast to these species it is early flowering.

Habitat: mostly grows singly in grassy phrygana, in open spaces, but also in thin forest (particularly on Rhodes, where it occurs in large populations). Grows happily in meadowy areas up to 1000 metres.

Hybrids: none known.

Confusion: unmistakable, even though very sturdy examples of *Orchis collina* sometimes resemble it in appearance; the flowers are very different.

Flowering period: beginning of II to beginning of IV.

Apella (KP), 21.3.1998

22

Ayios Isidoros (RH), 15.3.00

Ayios Pavlos (CR), 25.2.96

Ayios Isidoros (RH), 16.4.93

Festos (CR), 26.2.96

Diagnostics: plants often small, specimens with a few flowers only are often a mere 5 cms tall, but can reach to over 20 cms. There are supporting leaves, reducing in size progressively up the stem and enclosing it in a sheath-like manner, for the more than 20 flowers closely arranged on all sides of the stem. The flowers open to a lesser or greater degree depending on the weather conditions prevailing; they are a light pink to white in colour. The lip has, at its base, a definite spur which is only about 2 mm in length.

Habitat: endemic to Crete. Very rare, owing to a lack of suitable biotopes, which have been overgrazed. Grows at altitude (over 700 m) in mixed deciduous woodland, especially along gulleys which contain water, but also in dryer woodland consisting of Q. cerris. Occurs in all the high massifs.

Hybrids: none known.

Confusion: The appearance is unmistakable. The spur differentiates it from all other Cretan *Cephalanthera* species.

Epano Simi (CR), 20.5.01

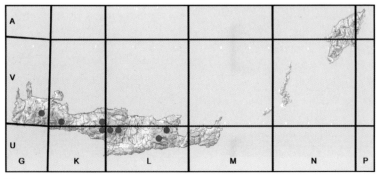

Biotope near Epano Simi (CR), 22.5.01

Selakano (CR), 21.5.01

Epano Simi (CR), 19.5.01

25

Cephalanthera epipactoides Fisch. & C.A.Mey.
Helleborine-like cephalanthera

Diagnostics: leaves distributed along the stem, inflorescence at the tip which is loose in shady locations, otherwise thickly-flowered. Lips clearly spurred at base. White flowers, sometimes tinged with delicate pink, mostly wide open. Lip white without any other colour.

Habitat: pine woodlands. To date, only a few plants have been found in the areas of pine woods on Rhodes, despite intensive research. These are probably the result of seeding from Turkey, where the species is common. Diffusion is to be expected.

Hybrids: not known from Rhodes and not to be expected. In Turkey, hybridisation with other species of *Cephalanthera*.

Confusion: the spurred lip and the shorter leaves distinguish it from *Cephalanthera longifolia* as a further variety of this genus from Rhodes.

Flowering period: middle to end of IV.

Kaş (Turkey), 10.5.88

Ayios Isidoros (RH), 12.5.1997

Ayios Isidoros (RH), 12.05.1997

Ayios Isidoros (RH), 12.5.1997

27

Cephalanthera longifolia (L.) FRITSCH
Long- or Sword-leaved Cephalanthera

Diagnostics: spike at the tip, long leaves, narrow to wide lanceolate, mostly pointing stiffly upward, enclosing the lower part of the inflorescence within their tips. Sepals brilliant white. Lip has an egg-yolk yellow fleck at its tip, no spur.

Habitat: woodland consisting of chestnut and Q. pubescens, mostly on acid subsoil in western Crete, where it also appears locally in small populations. Owing to a lack of suitable biotopes it is relatively rare on Crete, while on Rhodes it is only known from the coniferous forest biotope at Siana, where it was recently discovered. The variety is quite rare in the whole of the region.

Hybrids: not found in the region.

Confusion: differentiated from *Cephalanthera cucullata* and *Cephalanthera epipactoides* through a complete absence of spur, and through the inflorescence at the tip which has no bracts.

Flowering period: middle of IV to beginning of V.

Siana (RH), 20.4.98, H. JANSEN

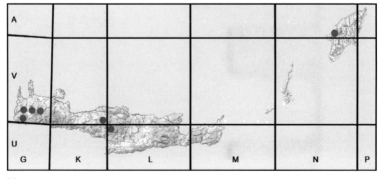

Single flowers, Konitsa (Greek mainland), 14.5.03

Ay. Irini (CR), 10.5.2001

Siana (RH), 15.5.1997

29

Comperia comperiana K.Koch
Filiform Orchid

Diagnostics: vigorous, tall plant related to the *Himantoglossum* genus with strong, loose flowers. 3-lobed lip, the lateral lobes ending in one - and the middle lobe in two - long thread-like tips, as a result the flowers can measure up to 6 cms in size.

Habitat: sparse pine woodland. Has not been observed on Rhodes with any certainty for several years. More recent information (see map) is based on supposed finds of rosettes, although these could not be corroborated by subsequent research at the potential time of flowering. Nevertheless, very large potential growing areas certainly exist, so that a rediscovery or a new occurrence may definitely be expected; the species occurs in neighbouring Turkey.

Hybrids: not known.

Confusion: unmistakable in view of the form of the flowers. Clearly differentiated during the flowering period from its relative, Barlia.

Flowering period: (estimated) end of IV to V.

Akseki (Turkey), 22.5.88

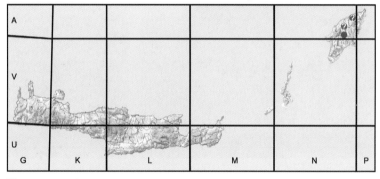

30

The centre of Rhodes presents a potentially excellent area for discovering this orchid 10.4.1995

Akseki (Turkey), 22.5.1988

Akseki (Turkey), 22.5.1988

Dactylorhiza romana (Sebast.) Soó
Roman Cuckoo Flower

Diagnostics: basal rosette of narrow, unflecked, lanceolate leaves. Flowers red, pink, whitish, yellow and all possible blends and variations of these colours. Lip with long, strong, upward-pointing spur, which is considerably longer than the ovary.

Habitat: on acid subsoil, mostly in bushy areas where there is heather or gorse.

Hybrids: not to be expected, on account of a lack of potential hybridisation partners.

Confusion: with some Orchid species in the region. Can be clearly differentiated from *Orchis anatolica* by its unspeckled leaves, while *Orchis laxiflora* has a quite differently-coloured flower and rilled, vertically-directed leaves.
Some specimen were found on Rhodes again in 2004.

Flowering period: end of III to middle of IV.

Angouseliana (CR), 4.4.94

Angouseliana (CR), 4.4.94

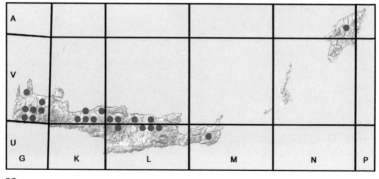

Angouseliana (CR), 4.4.1994

Angouseliana (CR), 4.4.1994

Sisarha (CR), 16.4.1992, W. LÜDERS

Sisarha (CR), 14.4.2001

33

Epipactis cretica KALOP. & ROBATSCH
Cretan Helleborine

Diagnostics: this autogamous, Cretan endemite is a dainty plant, mostly suffused with a delicate blue-violet colour. The leaves are small, less than 5 cm long, and the stem is only sparsely covered with hairs. The lowest leaf is a considerable distance from the ground. Hypochile and epichile sometimes have a reddish tinge, the epichile pointing forwards and slightly spade-shaped, but without bosses.

Habitat: the species grows in places that are free from leaves and vegetation along stream courses at higher altitudes (above 700 m), preferably in ravines where there is mixed woodland, on a calcareous soil. As a result of nibbling by goats, many plants never come to flower.

Hybrids: have been found with *Epipactis microphylla*.

Confusion: only possible with *Epipactis microphylla*, the stem of which is however, intensively covered with hairs. *Only E. microphylla has a wart-like boss on the outer lip.*

Flowering period: end of V to middle of VI.

Zaros (CR), 2.6.99, C. KREUTZ

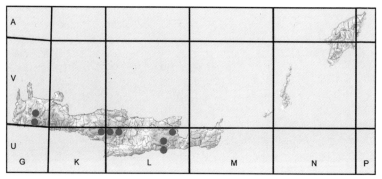

Biotope near Epano Simi (CR), 21.5.2001

Katharo (CR), 21.5.2001

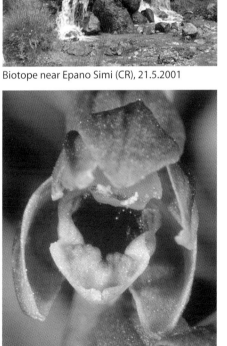

Zaros (CR), 2.6.1999, C. KREUTZ

Zaros (CR), 2.6.1999, C. KREUTZ

Epipactis microphylla (Ehrh.) Sw.
Small-leaved Helleborine

Diagnostics: the felt-like, hairy stems with mainly tiny leaves at the base are characteristic of this plant. The flowers have an intense aroma of vanilla; they mostly only open half-way and thus often hang bell-like on the stem. The epichile bears a whitish, warty boss. The petals are reddish coloured.

Habitat: has a wide Eurasian distribution. Can be found along shady banks of streams and in damp hollows, mostly in Chestnut woodlands but also beneath *Acer*. Because of its reliance on water it is not found in mountainous areas and only in western Crete does it flourish at an altitude of more than 500 metres.

Variation: considerable where height is concerned. Very vigorous examples around 50 cm tall have been found.

Confusion: only possible with *Epipactis cretica*. The felt-like, hairy stem and the epichile with its whitish warty boss are indicative.

Hybrids: with *Epipactis cretica*.

Flowering period: middle of V to middle of VI.

Ay. Irini (CR), 20.5.01

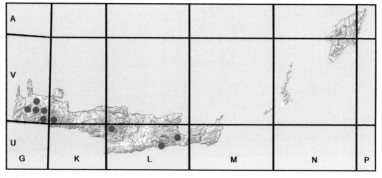

36

Strovles (CR), 11.5.2001

Strovles (CR), 11.5.2001

Biotope near Ay. Irini (CR), 10.5.2001

Himantoglossum samariense C. & A. ALIBERTIS
Cretan Himantoglossum

Diagnostics: strong plants, growing to over 50 cms in height and bearing up to 30 flowers which are arranged very loosely; the long lips stand out stiffly to the side. The middle lobe can be divided from just 2mm to a length of 18mm. The edge of the lip is undulate at the base up to the point where the 3-10 mm long lateral lobes project. The basic colour of the lip is a reddish-brown violet, with a green tinge. A white triangular area extends down from the beginning of the centre spur. Occasionally the humps at the beginning of the spur bear fine, red-violet dots, which sometimes also cover the white area. Its status as a species is a point of controversy.

Habitat: grows rarely in half-shade in sparse deciduous woodland or in stand of pines. Normally found at altitudes above 1000 metres, very rarely below.

Hybrids: not known.

Confusion: hardly possible.

Xyloskalon (CR), 22.5.01

Xyloskalon (CR), 18.5.2001

Epano Simi (CR), 22.5.2001

Laki (CR), 22.5.2001

Xyloskalon CR), 14.5.2001

39

Limodorum abortivum (L.) Sw.
Violet Limodore

Diagnostics: frequently large, vigorous plants without green leaves and only a few violet scale-leaves enclosing the stems. Large flowers, sepals whitish-violet, steel blue to red-violet, occasionally almost white but in some places also pinkish-red (this variation has already been found in several examples on Rhodes). Lip of a darker, mostly blue-violet, long-spurred, with the spur pointing in a steep downwards direction.

Habitat: mostly in woodlands of *Pinus brutia*, also in chestnut groves and taller phrygana in western Crete, sometimes in open spaces. While it is often found on Rhodes in large populations, it is relatively rare on Crete because pine afforestation is rare. More common on Karpathos, but only flowers sparingly in dry years.

Hybrids: not known.

Confusion: unmistakable.

Siana (RH), 15.5.97

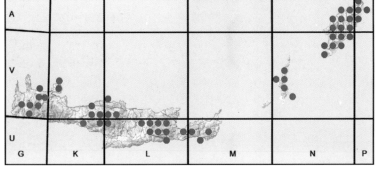

Ay. Isidoros (RH), 12.5.1997

Laerma (RH), 19.3.2002

Thripti (KR), 8.5.1997

Listera ovata L.
Common Twayblade

Diagnostics: two large, oval, leaves opposite one another on a short, strong stem several centimetres above the ground. From between these leaves there extends a spike along which on all sides, numerous small completely green flowers without spurs are carried. The petals however can exhibit a reddish tinge. Nectar forms at the base of the lip and trickles downwards, thus forming a shining stripe in the middle of the lip.

Habitat: only on Crete where, along the courses of streams, in damp ravines, beside water-filled gulleys in chestnut woodlands, on both acid and basic subsoils at altitudes of between 400 and 1200 metres, it is only found very rarely, in contrast to its frequent occurrence in central Europe.

Hybrids: not known.

Epano Simi (CR), 21.5.01

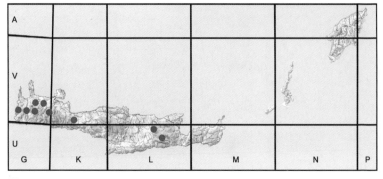

Biotope near Epano Simi (CR), 21.5.2001

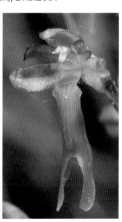

Epano Simi (CR), 21.5.2001   Epano Simi (CR), 21.5.2001   Epano Simi (CR), 21.5.2001

43

Neotinea maculata (DESF.) STEARN
Dense-flowered Orchid

Diagnostics: small, elegant plants, with the middle leaves of the rosette clasping the stem in the manner of a sheath. Dark green leaves, mostly speckled, and often suffused with red on the edges and undersides. The rosette already develops in late autumn and produces the flowerhead at the end of the vegetation phase. Thick spikes of small, whitish to deep-pink coloured flowers, lip divided into three lobes. The middle lobe is divided once more into two short points at the tip. The centre part is speckled in red-violet, but rarely it can be just plain.

Habitat: widely distributed species, which also occurs on the island of Gavdos, the southernmost point in Europe. In the region it is found in sparse pine woodland, often in half-shade on slopes. It flourishes on acid or superficially acid subsoils and can be found up to altitudes of more than 1300 metres.

Hybrids: none known.

Confusion: not possible.

Flowering period: end of III to end of IV.

Lastos (KP), 20.3.01

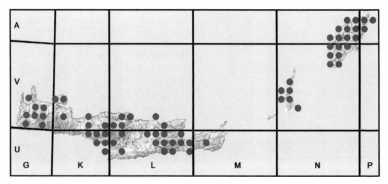

Akramitis (RH), 27.3.2000

Volada (KP), 21.3.2001

Melambes (CR), 20.4.1993

Ophrys aegaea KALTEISEN & H.R.REINHARD
Aegean Ophrys

Diagnostics: strong, stocky plants, mostly only with 2-3 flowers and rarely as many as 7. Pink sepals with a green central vein, petals spatula-shaped, slightly darker, about 2/3 the length of the sepals. Lip round in outline, large, extending almost flat, with the edges of the lips not thrown back. Transverse oval-shaped stigmatic cavity divided by a brown horizontal line, of which the upper half is white, and the lower half often suffused with sky-blue. Velvety lip, with slightly longer hairs towards the shoulder, dark red-brown, often a patchy light orange-red towards the middle and the base. An actual basal field is absent. Blazon consists of two whitish to metallic blue fields.

Habitat: sparse pine woodland, seldom in grassy phrygana, also in *Phlomis*-fields, on basic soil. Since it occurs on Amorgos, it cannot be designated as endemic to Karpathos.

Hybrids: with *Ophrys cretica* ssp. *ariadnae, Ophrys ferrum-equinum.*

Confusion: with hybrids with *Ophrys ferrum-equinum.*

Flowering period: end of II to end of III.

Apella (KP), 21.3.00

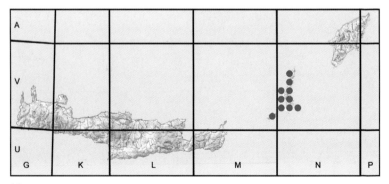

Apella (KP), 20.3.2000

Apella (KP), 21.3.2000

Apella (KP), 21.3.2000

47

Ophrys apifera HUDS.
Bee Ophrys

Diagnostics: sepals whitish-green to pinkish-red, petals short and narrow, extended connective appendage at end of pistil-column. The blazon is orange, edged in yellowish-white, the lateral lobes thickly haired; the lip apex is completely thrown back. This species is self-pollinating: already in the early stages of flowering the pollen sacs fold down over the stigma, as can clearly be seen in the picture.

Habitat: meadowy pastureland, open olive groves, marshes near the sea, grows well in areas that are alternately damp and dry.

Hybrids: stands alone because of its flowering period and self-pollination; no hybrids observed in the region to date.

Flowering period: end of III to middle of V.

Confusion: differentiated from most other species of *Ophrys* through its flowering period, and additionally through the thrown-back tip of the lip, which distinguishes it from species in the *Ophrys episcopalis* group.

Malia (CR), 14.4.01

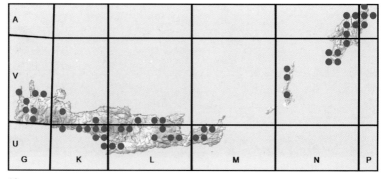

Malia (CR), 14.4.2001

Mournes (CR), 17.5.2001

Arhipoli (RH), 14.5.1997

Festos (CR), 14.4.1994

49

Ophrys bombyliflora LINK
Bumblebee Ophrys

Diagnostics: green sepals, spatula-like petals, hairy. Small, three-lobed lip, blackish-brown, rarely lighter in colour, only hazily- bordered light grey lip blazon. Lateral lobes bear dark hairs. Deep, wide, black stigmatic cavity, whose edges are framed with black ridges. The flowers are few and project at right angles to the stem. The species forms vegetative tubers, so that groups of plants are often found. The plants which occur on Rhodes are characterised by particularly small lips.

Habitat: alternately dry and wet places in phrygana, marshes near the sea, often together with *Orchis laxiflora*, always on open ground.

Hybrids: rarely with *Ophrys cretica* ssp. *ariadnae, Ophrys heldreichii, Ophrys spruneri* ssp. *spruneri, Ophrys tenthredinifera, Ophrys umbilicata* ssp. *rhodia.*

Confusion: hardly possible.

Flowering period: end of III to middle of IV.

Laerma (RH), 15.3.2002

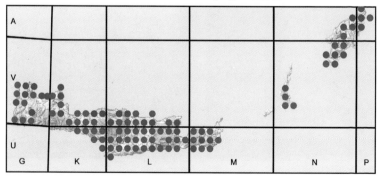

Stoli (CR), 31.3.1994

Lastos (KP), 21.3.2001

Agia Varvara (CR), 25.3.1994

Lardos (RH), 11.4.1993

Ophrys cretica (Vierh.) E.Nelson
ssp. *ariadnae* (Paulus) H.Kretzschmar
Ariadne's Ophrys

Diagnostics: green sepals, often with a reddish tinge, red-brown petals. Basic colour of lip deep black, rarely dark brown. Three-lobed lip, the middle lobe bare in the centre but bearing fine, short hairs on the edge; roundish lateral lobes with markedly longer hairs. Stigmatic cavity white with a black horizontal line, either as high as it is wide or higher. Lip bears a whitish, H-shaped blazon emanating from the base, often degenerating into a patchy, irregular linear marking.

Habitat: phrygana, meadow areas, open olive groves. Common on Karpathos and in Central Crete. Becoming rarer in the extreme east and west of Crete.

Hybrids: with *Ophrys aegeae, Ophrys bombyliflora, Ophrys cretica* ssp. *cretica, Ophrys ferrum-equinum, Ophrys fusca* ssp. *creberrima, Ophrys heldreichii, Ophrys mammosa, Ophrys phryganae, O. sphegodes* ssp. *cretensis, Ophrys spruneri* (both subspecies).

Flowering period: from the middle of II to the beginning of IV.

Confusion: with other subspecies of *Ophrys cretica*. Differentiated by the narrower stigmatic cavity, the height of which exceeds the width.

Pigadia (KP), 18.3.00

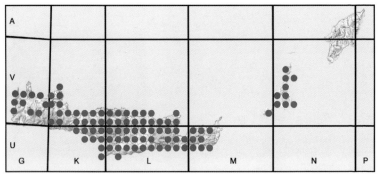

Ano Viannos (CR), 5.4.1992

Ayios Mamas (KA), 22.3.01, a local population markedly different in its appearance, transitional between ssp. *ariadne* and ssp. *cretica*.

Ag. Varvara (CR), 27.3.1994

53

Ophrys cretica (Vierh.) E. Nelson
ssp. *beloniae* H. & G.Kretzschmar
Belonia subspecies of the Cretan Ophrys

Diagnostics: sepals pink to pinkish-red, rarely whitish, petals dark red. Basic colour of lip deep black, velvet-haired, with thick blunt side humps, hairless on the lip side. H-shaped blazon emanating from the base of the lip, further lines often extend out onto the rounded lip humps. Linear marking of the blazon framed in brilliant white, enclosing reddish-violet areas. Stigmatic cavity wider than it is high, in the upper, white area with a black transverse line terminating in two 'eyes' which are additionally framed by parts of the lip blazon.

Habitat: phrygana, often beneath thorny burnet, in open spaces.

Hybrids: with *Ophrys mammosa*, *Ophrys reinholdii*.

Confusion: hardly possible (due its distribution), but if at all with *Ophrys reinholdii*, which can be differentiated because of its markings.

Flowering period: middle of II to end of III.

Plimiri (RH), 29.3.2000

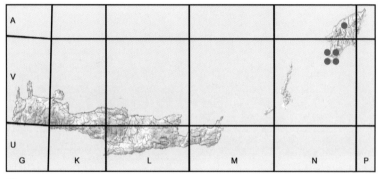

Kattavia (RH), 28.3.2000

Kattavia (RH), 24.3.2000

Kattavia (RH), 24.3.2000

Kattavia (RH), 24.3.2000

55

Ophrys cretica (VIERH.) E.NELSON
ssp. *bicornuta* H.KRETZSCHMAR & R.JAHN
Two-horned Cretan Ophrys

Diagnostics: sepals whitish to pinkish-red, also greenish with a red tinge, petals red to red-brown. Basic colour of lip deep, velvety black to black-brown, with sharply-pointed horns, directed forwards and to the sides, which are often hairless and lighter in colour towards the middle lobe. H-shaped striped blazon of the lip, often without any contact to the base of the lip, frequently enclosing small blue or violet, hairless areas. The linear marking is limited to the middle lobe and does not extend over the side humps. The stigmatic cavity is a wide horizontal oval in shape, white, and sharply defined from the deep-black lip through a black horizontal line above the white to sky-blue edged pseudo-eyes, which are connected by another, broken sky-blue to red-violet horizontal line.

Analipsi (CR), 17.4.03

Flowering period: beginning of III to beginning of IV.

Habitat: in phrygana and open spaces below 500 metres in the eastern part of Crete.

Hybrids: with *Ophrys sphegodes* ssp. *cretensis*, *Ophrys spruneri* ssp. *spruneri*.

Confusion: can be differentiated from ssp. *ariadne* through its large stigma cavity, and from other subspecies through its pointed lateral humps.

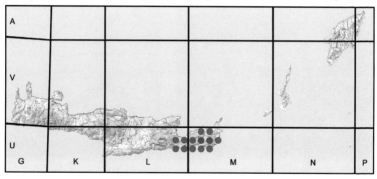

Analipsi (CR), 17.4.2003

Ierapetra (CR), 22.3.1993

Analipsi (CR), 17.4.2003,

Analipsi (CR), 17.4.2003

57

Ophrys cretica (Vierh.) E.Nelson
ssp. *cretica*
Common Cretan Ophrys

Ierapetra (CR), 17.4.003

Diagnostics: green sepals, sometimes with a reddish tinge, rarely pink, petals greenish to red-brown. Basic colour of lip black to dark brownish-black. Three-lobed lip, middle lobe hairless in the centre, fine short hairs on the edges. Stigmatic cavity white, divided by a horizontal black line, its breadth clearly greater than its height. The H-shaped, white linear blazon of the lip often encloses small, blue-violet areas in its lower section. The lateral lobes stand out towards the side, and have no pointed humps. It flowers later than the ssp. *ariadnae*.

Habitat: phrygana, dry meadow areas, open olive groves at altitudes of less than 500 metres.

Flowering period: beginning to end of IV.

Hybrids: with *Ophrys cretica* ssp. *ariadnae*, *Ophrys sphegodes* ssp. *gortynia*, *Ophrys heldreichii*, *Ophrys mammosa*.

Confusion: differentiated from the ssp. *bicornuta* through its smaller, strongly-divided lip without horns, and by its flowering period.

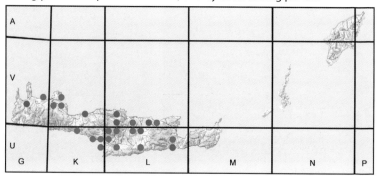

Ierapetra (CR), 17.4.2003

Ag. Galini (CR), 14.4.2003

Ag. Galini (CR), 14.4.2003

Ag. Galini (CR), 14.4.2003

Ierapetra (CR), 19.4.2003

59

Ophrys episcopalis - *oestrifera* group

Ophrys candica
Ophrys dodekanensis
Ophrys episcopalis
Ophrys heldreichii
Ophrys oestrifera

The beginning of any description of this group should really include a discussion of the nomenclature applicable to it. As this would go beyond the scope of a paperback edition, the reader is directed to the observations in KRETZSCHMAR et al. 2001 and KRETZSCHMAR et al. 2002. With Ophrys minoa (C. &A. ALIBERTIS), P. DELFORGE, *Ophrys lyciensis* PAULUS, E.GÜGEL, D.&U. RÜCKBRODT, *Ophrys helios* C.A.J. KREUTZ, *Ophrys halia* PAULUS further genera from the southern Aegean have been added to the list of species; of these however, in our opinion and given the high variability within their populations *Ophrys minoa* and *Ophrys lyciensis* are to be seen as synonyms for *Ophrys candica, Ophrys helios* and *Ophrys halia* for *Ophrys episcopalis*, and *Ophrys cornutula* for *Ophrys oestrifera*. In addition the whole group is characterised, not only by its high variability, but also by frequent hybridogenous 'scrambling' of the species, in particular on Rhodes.

Ophrys candica, the first species of the group, has not been found on Karpathos or Kasos to date. It is relatively isolated on Crete because of its late flowering period, and on Rhodes it clearly flowers earlier in relation to other species. Horned or otherwise variously marked forms are simply to be categorised as conspicuous variations.

Ophrys dodekanensis is unmistakable due to its small flowers, its appearance (habit) and its conspicuous colouring. This extremely early flowering species remained unknown for a long time, since at the usual time when travel is undertaken, at the beginning of April, it is only to be found still at the highest locations on Prof. Ilias, and mostly only hybridised with *Ophrys oestrifera* or *Ophrys episcopalis* (see right). This explains the varying details given for other small-flowered species (*Ophrys minutula* GÖLZ & H. R. REINHARD, *Ophrys holoserica* ssp. *heterochila* RENZ & TAUBENHEIM) in a number of publications about

Prof. Ilias (RH), 29.3.2002

Rhodes. *Ophrys dodekanensis* makes a notably stable appearance on Rhodes and in neighbouring areas of Turkey and occurs in considerable populations in the central part of Rhodes; these are in full flower from the end of February to the middle of March.

Ophrys episcopalis is a large-flowered form, closely- related to the family of *Ophrys holoserica* of central Europe. Plants of this type are found on all three islands, with specimens of both large and normal-sized flowers together at the same place.

Neither during the flowering period nor on ecological grounds is it possible to make a clear division between these populations; the occurrence of large flowers on many plants seems rather to be a fortuitous feature. Not infrequently, additional transitional forms to *Ophrys heldreichii* can be found; such plants are especially common on Kasos.

The fact that quite different pollinators are found in the region from those in Central Europe can, nevertheless, be taken into consideration as an argument concerning the differentiation between plants of the southern Aegean and those of Central Europe. This has led us to designate the plants on Rhodes, where large-flowered specimens clearly dominate, as an isolate (reproductive community) under the name of *Ophrys episcopalis* (KRETZSCHMAR et al. 2001: 85). Such populations, mixed where the size of their flowers is concerned, are also found on Crete, Kasos and Karpathos. Since conditions on these islands do not differ basically from those on Rhodes, we also use the designation *Ophrys episcopalis* there.

Without question there are local divergences to be found; these are to be evaluated under the notion of clusters (cf. KRETZSCHMAR et al. 2001: 27-8). It does not seem justified to accord such small numbers of plants a special status, even when the biological mechanism of pollination might seem to have changed due to the relative isolation of such populations.

Ophrys heldreichii is very well differentiated. It occurs on all three islands and is one of the most common species. The size of the flowers is highly variable, and sometimes plants with smaller flowers occur (almost always together with specimens which have normal-sized flowers). Transitions to *Ophrys episcopalis* are common.

The last of the group, only found on Rhodes, is *Ophrys oestrifera*. It is often intermixed with *Ophrys heldreichii*, especially in the north and centre of the island. Towards the more arid south of the island the populations become increasingly uniform and have smaller (to very small) flowers with a simultaneous increase in the length of the horns of the lip.

Possible occasional mentions of finds of *Ophrys bornmuelleri*, in particular on Karpathos, refer to such divergent individual plants. The possibility cannot, however, be excluded that seeds of this species have occasionally 'flown in' from the north (in the central and southern Cyclades related plants are found in the variation of this group designated *Ophrys andria*). The occurrence of a homogeneous population of *Ophrys bornmuelleri* sensu stricto in the region is, however, most probably to be discounted.

Ophrys candica Greuter, Matthäs & Risse
White Ophrys

Diagnostics: undivided lip, with strong humps (but sometimes without); very variable form. Lip edged all round with long brown hairs growing forewords very strongly. Blazon patchy, hairless, with violet as its basic colour, wide whitish edge, linear marking often also radiating inwards into the blazon area. Sepals flowery, petals very short and triangular. The plant is often tall, but mostly more delicate than *Ophrys episcopalis* or *Ophrys heldreichii*, and its flowers are smaller than those of the two latter species.

Habitat: on basic subsoil, in bushy zones in areas of meadow, meadow phrygana, and in thin woodland, to altitudes of over 1300 metres.

Confusion: possible with the frequent transitional forms to other species within the group, but relatively isolated occurrences due to the late period of flowering.

Hybrids: with *Ophrys dodekanensis*, *Ophrys heldreichii* and *Ophrys episcopalis*.

Flowering time: from the end of III on Rhodes. From the middle of IV to the end of V on Crete.

Ayios Isidoros (RH), 8.4.95.

Apollona, (RH), 12.5.1997

Drimiskos (CR), 17.5.2001

Ag. Isidoros (RH), 8.4.1995

Laerma, (RH), 16.4.1995

Ag. Vasilios (CR), 11.4.2001

Ophrys dodekanensis H.KRETZSCHMAR & KREUTZ
Dodecanese Ophrys

Diagnostics: small plants, flower-bearing stem rarely over 20 cms in height. Conspicuously large by comparison is the leaf rosette, which can have a diameter of nearly 20 cms. Very small flowers, lip mostly less than 10 mm in length, characterised by its orange to orange-brown basal field and a dark brown horizontal line on the conspicuously wide stigmatic cavity. The lip is mostly deeply three-lobed, sometimes however incompletely divided or even has a continuous edge. The lateral humps are pointed and covered with long brown hairs as well as the whole edge of the lip. The blazon takes many forms and consists of yellowish lines which frame the basal field. The petals are narrow, short, spatula-shaped and pink, the sepals are mostly white, more rarely pink to pinkish-red, and are directed backwards; the central vein is green.

Habitat: thin areas of pine woodland, bushy phrygana.

Hybrids: with *Ophrys umbilicata* ssp. *rhodia* and the other species in the group.

Flowering period: beginning of II to beginning of IV.

Laerma (RH), 26.2.97.

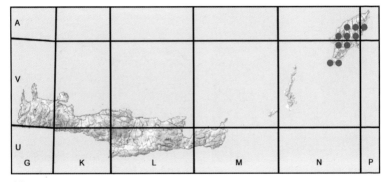

Laerma (RH), 26.2.1997

Laerma (RH), 26.2.1997

Laerma (RH), 26.2.1997

Profitis Ilias (RH), 3.4.1995

Laerma (RH), 26.2.1997

Ophrys episcopalis Poir.
Large-flowered Bee Ophrys

Diagnostics: plants up to 50 cm high. Breadth of the lip very variable, from 10 to 20 mm. Outline undivided, with longer hairs in shoulder area, towards the front only short and velvety. Lip either flat or with strong humps in shoulder area. Blazon very variable, yellowish-white to metallic, enclosing a lighter coloured basal field. Strong, forward and upward-pointing lip outgrowth. Whitish-pink to pinkish-red sepals, short petals, triangular, mostly of a darker colour than the sepals.

Habitat: requires damper ground than other species, thus it thrives in damp hollows that are in the process of drying out, in old, terraced olive groves and in meadow phrygana.

Hybrids: with all species of the group, also with *Ophrys ferrumequinum*, *Ophrys spruneri* ssp. *spruneri*, *Ophrys tenthredinifera*, *Ophrys umbilicata*.

Confusion: typically unmistakable, but problems may be caused by the variability and frequent hybridisation.

Flowering period: beginning of III to end of IV.

Drimiskos (CR), 12.4.01

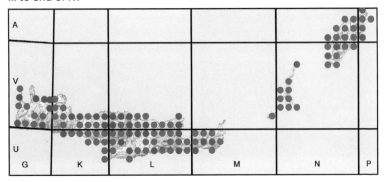

Fri (KA), 28.3.2001

Apella (KP), 25.3.2001

Faliraki (RH), 12.4.1983

67

Ophrys heldreichii Schltr.
Heldreich's Ophrys

Diagnostics: pinkish-red sepals, petals about half their length, narrow and spatula-shaped. Billowing edge of the lip, with the greatest width clearly below the base of the middle lobe, which has a very strong, forward-directed protuberance at its tip. The strong humps on the side lobes end in a point towards the front.

Habitat: bushy phrygana, areas of meadow, open spaces. One of the most common species on each of the main islands. Concentrated mostly in the northern part of Rhodes, while *Ophrys oestrifera* dominates in the south of the island.

Hybrids: with the species of this group, also with *Ophrys bombyliflora, Ophrys cretica* ssp. *ariadnae, Ophrys tenthredinifera, Ophrys ferrum-equinum, Ophrys umbilicata* ssp. *rhodia*.

Confusion: particularly easy on Rhodes with the common hybrids formed with the other species of the group, but unmistakable in its typical form through the size of the flowers and the lip which billows out in a downwards direction.

Flowering period: end of III to end of IV.

Sternes (CR), 5.4.94

Goudouras (CR), 30.3.1994

Lachania (RH), 10.4.1993

Sternes (CR), 5.4.1994

Ophrys oestrifera M.BIEB.
Brake Ophrys

Diagnostics: slim, tall plant, often with many flowers. Lip clearly smaller than in *Ophrys heldreichii*, sometimes very small. Outline of lip is three-lobed, lateral lobes are covered in thick brown hair at the base and end in long, pointed protuberances. Middle lobe has its greatest width above the middle; the yellowish blazon encloses (towards the base of the lip) a basal field which is distinguished by its orange-brown colour. On the area of the lip there is a bare region, red-violet in colour. The pinkish-red sepals are twice as long as the dark red petals.

Habitat: bushy phrygana, coastal phrygana, damp places in meadow areas.

Hybrids: with *Ophrys umbilicata* ssp. *rhodia*, and with other species in the group.

Flowering period: middle of III to end of IV.

Confusion: difficult to differentiate hybrid forms, particularly with *Ophrys heldreichii*. Attention should be paid to the size of the flowers and the form of the lip, with the greatest breadth above the middle.

Kattavia (RH), 17.3.02

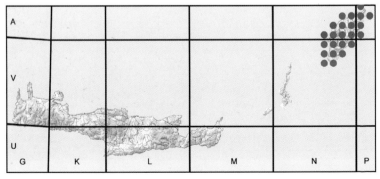

Kattavia (RH), 5.4.1995

Prof. Ilias (RH), 3.4.1995

Pilona (RH), 19.3.2002

Ophrys ferrum-equinum DESF.
Horseshoe Ophrys

Diagnostics: plant varies greatly with regard to the size and form of its flowers. Sepals pinkish-red to whitish-green, petals long, spatula-shaped and red. Lip coloured deep black, sometimes blackish-red, dark and velvety in appearance and with only short hairs, no humps, edges of lip turned downwards, also standing up in places, sometimes +/- three lobes. Length of the lip very variable between 10 and 16 mm. Blazon in the form of a horseshoe or even just appearing as double stripes in metallic grey, blue or sometimes reddish-violet, occasionally thinly edged in white.

Habitat: in phrygana, in thin pine woodlands, always on alkaline soil.

Flowering period: beginning of III to beginning of IV.

Hybrids: with *Ophrys aegeae, Ophrys cretica* ssp. *ariadnae, Ophrys episcopalis, Ophrys heldreichii, Ophrys lucis, Ophrys reinholdi, Ophrys speculum.*

Confusion: with dark-coloured specimens of *Ophrys aegea*; it also hybridises easily with the latter.

Ay. Mamas (KA), 19.3.00

Laerma (RH), 19.3.2002

Laerma (RH), 19.3.2002

Laerma (RH), 19.3.2002

Laerma (RH), 19.3.2002

The Ophrys fusca group

By reason of its great distribution, *Ophrys fusca* ssp. *leucadica* can be viewed as the eastern Mediterranean common ancestor of this group. It occurs in varying form on Rhodes, Kasos and Karpathos, but typically is not found on Crete. It is probable that the particular geographical actuality on Crete has led *Ophrys fusca* in its strictest sense to establish itself in several well-distinguishable subspecies which inhabit places that are environmentally different from one another. This has prompted PAULUS (1998), to describe a total of four new species for Crete. These four, however, constitute only points of reference, as it were, for development. Numerous mixed populations underline the fact that even here the process of the differentiation of species has not been completed to date. The hypothetical relationships of the group are shown in the table (following). By taking as points of departure the three 'common ancestors' *Ophrys iricolor*, the eastern Mediterranean subspecies of *Ophrys fusca*, and *Ophrys omegaifera*, the other species can hypothetically be placed in order.

The subspecies *thriptiensis* is small in size and flowers extremely early (before all the other orchids); it is found on the great heights east of Thripti. The large-flowering, flat-lipped ssp. *creticola* also flowers very early, roughly together with *Ophrys sphegodes* ssp. *cretensis*. The flowering period overlaps at the end with that of ssp. *creberrima*, whereby hybrid populations are created. Ssp. *creberrima* is common locally in southern Crete. ssp. *cressa* poses greater difficulties. It has been described as "*late Ophrys fusca*" from Thripti in eastern Crete. Similar, relatively late-flowering populations can, however, also be found in the peak areas of many mountains in southern Crete. Although there are considerable local divergences between them, all of these late-flowering populations are characterised by flat, extended lip edges and a narrow, yellow-edged lip of medium-size without a fold at the base; for this reason all these populations have been designated ssp. *cressa* in KRETZSCHMAR et al. 2002.

Local Taxa have also been differentiated on Rhodes, and have been newly described in the species range by PAULUS (2001). The particular conditions on Rhodes have to be taken into account here, since the work of Italian foresters during the first half of the last century brought about huge upheavals in the natural vegetation. Instead of the natural sclerophyllous vegetation they planted large areas of pine monoculture; forest fires repeatedly destroyed huge sections of these areas. The effect of an explosion of tourism can currently be observed in the coastal areas in the form of gross encroachments on the land; the southern tip of Rhodes is used over a wide area by the military as a tank practice area. These huge assaults on the countryside have helped the orchids as successional plants towards a really explosive multiplication locally; this can be seen again and again in areas where fires have raged. The formation of diverse, locally homogeneous small Taxa by means of cluster-building thus receives the maximum encouragement. It does not seem to serve any purpose to list these small Taxa, of which there

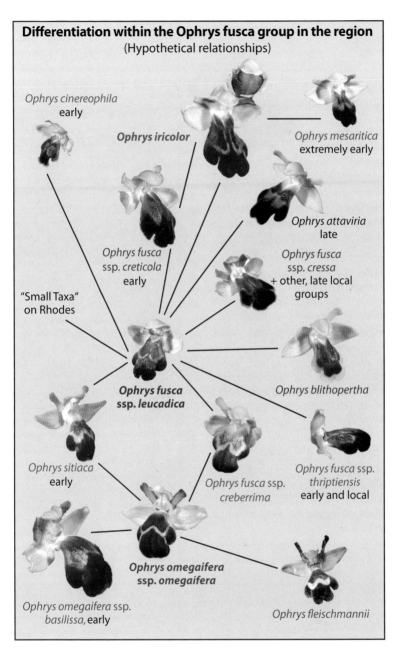

Differentiation within the Ophrys fusca group in the region
(Hypothetical relationships)

Ophrys cinereophila
early

Ophrys iricolor

Ophrys mesaritica
extremely early

Ophrys attaviria
late

Ophrys fusca
ssp. creticola
early

Ophrys fusca
ssp. cressa
+ other, late local
groups

"Small Taxa"
on Rhodes

**Ophrys fusca
ssp. leucadica**

Ophrys blithopertha

Ophrys sitiaca
early

Ophrys fusca ssp.
creberrima

Ophrys fusca ssp.
thriptiensis
early and local

**Ophrys omegaifera
ssp. omegaifera**

Ophrys omegaifera ssp.
basilissa, early

Ophrys fleischmannii

are many more on the island, as species. They are retained as synonymous forms, even if special relationships with pollinators might have been developed. It is exactly this plethora of new, local sightings which makes their importance increasingly questionable where the differentiation of species is concerned and a coincidental, local relationship more probable.

Ophrys attaviria D.RÜCKBRODT & WENKER

Attaviria Ophrys

Diagnostics: slim, tall plants. The lip has a deep groove at the base, it is large and flat and stands rather away from the stem. Blazon contains a large amount of blue. The species, through its colouring, resembles a small *Ophrys iricolor* but the underside of the lip is green.

Habitat: phrygana, in sparse forest/woodland margins, often in areas where there have previously been forest fires.

Hybrids: no definite examples known, if transitional forms to the other Taxa of the group are not taken into account.

Confusion: possible with other species in the group, but from the point of view of appearance most likely with *Ophrys iricolor*, although it is clearly differentiated through the green underside of the lip and it's late flowering period during which only the yellow-edged *Ophrys blitopertha* is otherwise still in flower. The question of whether or not it is endemic to Rhodes must be addressed by further research.

Flowering period: beginning to end of IV.

Embonas (RH), 4.4.1995

Kattavia (RH), 2.4.1995

Siana (RH), 15.5.1997

Laerma (RH), 31.3.2001

Ophrys blitopertha PAULUS & GACK
Beetle Ophrys

Diagnostics: late-flowering species, with relatively large flowers. Lip edged in a wide yellow or orange band. The edge of the lip is not turned downwards, but flat or slightly turned upwards. Plants may have a very strong stem.

Habitat: phrygana, characteristically on well-grazed areas. Flowers usually open when grazing has ceased because of a lack of adequate plant growth.

Hybrids: with *Ophrys cinereophila*.

Confusion: possibly with the similarly yellow-edged but much earlier-flowering *Ophrys cinereophila*, the flowers of which are however, clearly smaller and have a strong downwards fold in the front part of the lip. There is however a mixed Taxon which is an intermediary between these two species in

Ayios Isidoros (RH), 10.4.95

an area to the west of Lardos on Rhodes which is now greening over after suffering forest fires. The picture taken on 29.3.00 originates from a point where the climatic conditions are extremely advantageous. On Rhodes, *Ophrys blitopertha* is easily differentiated from the other Taxa.

Flowering period: beginning to end of IV.

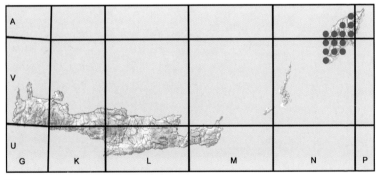

Arnitha (RH), 15.4.1993

Mesanagros (RH), 5.4.1995

Laerma (RH), 29.3.2000

Lardos(RH), 16.4.1993

Kattavia (RH), 31.3.2001

Ophrys cinereophila PAULUS & GACK
Small-flowered brown Ophrys

Diagnostics: early blooming species with small flowers. Lip edged in yellow, clearly folded downwards at or just above the middle of the lip, Blazon often of an intense blue, definite groove at base of lip. A conspicuous feature is the large size of the fruit in relation to the small flowers.

Habitat: pine woodlands, bushy phrygana, recultivated woodland or previous in areas where there have been forest fires. In classic phrygana only when the subsoil provides enough moisture or the cover has grown to a protective height. Requires basic subsoil and is found from the coast up to a height of around 900 metres. Common on all the islands.

Hybrids: only rarely with the subspecies of *Ophrys fusca*.

Confusion: as a rule clearly differentiated from the subspecies of *Ophrys fusca* by the size of the flowers, also by the colour and shape of the markedly folded lip with its narrow yellow edge.

Flowering period: middle of II to end of III.

Piles (KP), 18.3.00

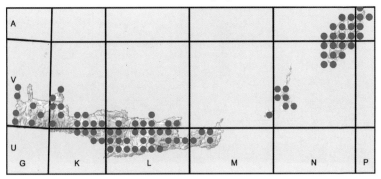

80

Melambes (CR), 25.2.1996

Laerma (RH), 15.3.2000

Spoa (KP), 20.3.2000

Laerma (RH), 29.3.2002

Ophrys fleischmannii Hayek
Fleischmann's Ophrys

Stavrohorio (CR), 10.4.93

Diagnostics: small plants, delicate, often only around 10 cm high, with few flowers. Lip without a groove at the base, lightly folded, with whitish-grey long hairs on a black-brown surface. The area of the metallic or brown-violet blazon has shorter hairs or is almost hairless, and is bordered towards the front by a wide, light-coloured "omega".

Habitat: frequent in the mountains of eastern Crete, in pine woodlands, also in open phrygana. Only on basic subsoil.

Hybrids: with *Ophrys iricolor*. Transitional forms to *Ophrys omegaifera* in eastern Crete.

Confusion: possible with *Ophrys omegaifera*. Differentiated through the weak fold at the base of the lip, the smaller flowers and the longer whitish hairs which also cover the area of the blazon.

Flowering period: middle of III to middle of IV.

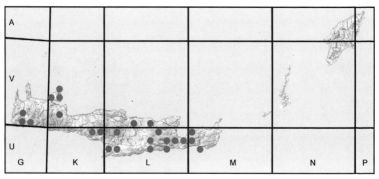

Sougia (CR), 10.4.2001

Orino (CR), 10.4.1993

Ophrys fusca LINK
ssp. *creberrima* (PAULUS) H. KRETZSCHMAR
Creberrima Ophrys

Diagnostics: up to 5 me-dium-sized flowers, with the edges of the lips turned downwards. Lip has a groove at the base, with the edge of the groove thrown up in a flattish swelling which appears more pronounced because of the fold of the lip at the base. Blazon has a wide, intense blue to whit-ish border in the form of a flat omega; this border may be coloured from an intense blue to whitish. The base encloses an area which is often speckled in bluish-grey, and sometimes of a uniform silver-grey or blue colour.

Habitat: grassy phrygana, areas of meadow, open ol-ive groves up to an altitude of around 900 metres.

Flowering period: begin-ning of III to IV.

Hybrids: transitional popu-lations with ssp. *cressa* and ssp. *creticola*.

Melambes (CR), 18.4.93

Confusion: differentiated from ssp. cressa, which has smaller flowers, and ssp. creticola (the flowers of which are slightly larger), by the edge of the lip which is turned downwards and backwards.

Saktouria (CR), 29.3.1994 - plants which exhibit a partly hybridogenous influence

Melambes (CR), 2.4.1994

Saktouria (CR), 2.3.1996

85

Ophrys fusca Link
ssp. *cressa* (Paulus) H. Kretzschmar
Cressa Ophrys

Diagnostics: delicate plants, mostly less than 15 cms and only rarely up to 25 cms in height. Leaves have mostly gone by the time of flowering. Medium-sized flowers, late blooming variety, flowering around the same time as *Anacamptis pyramidalis*. Lip is only arched, without a fold, base of lip has a deep groove. The strong yellow edges of the lip spread out flat and can be highly variable in width. The central area of the lip is completely framed in silver-blue or only blue, while it is coloured reddish-brown towards the base.

Habitat: meadowy, open phrygana, only at higher altitudes from 500 to 1300 metres, probably not found in low-lying areas. Only on basic subsoil.

Hybrids: forms mixed populations with ssp. *creberrima*.

Confusion: differentiated from the other Taxa by its flat lip and late flowering period.

Flowering period: beginning of IV to the middle of V.

Miamou (CR), 20.4.00

Thripti (CR), 8.5.1997

Gerakari (CR), 17.5.2001
Transition to ssp. *creberirima*

Thripti (CR), 8.5.1997

Ophrys fusca LINK
ssp. *creticola* (PAULUS) H. KRETZSCHMAR
Creticola Ophrys

Diagnostics: strong, squat plants, with a maximum of 4 very large flowers which are only slightly smaller than those of *Ophrys iricolor*. Early flowering, just slightly later than *Ophrys sphegodes* ssp. *cretensis*. Lip only slightly arched, without a fold, deep groove at base of lip. Edges of lip spread out flat with weak division into lateral lobes. Edge mostly red-brown, sometimes thinly bordered in yellow. Centre of the lip framed in silver-blue or just blue, reddish-brown in colour towards the base. Endemic to Crete, flowering before *Anemone coronaria*.

Habitat: meadows and fields, open phrygana to an altitude of 900 metres, only on basic soil.

Hybrids: transitional forms to ssp. *creberrima*.

Kerames (CR), 2.3.96

Confusion: similar to *ssp. cressa* in the appearance of its flowers, the lips of which are spread out flat, but the flowers are much larger. All other subspecies can be differentiated through a fold in the lip or the edges of the lip turned downwards.

Flowering period: middle of II to middle of III.

Kerames (CR), 2.3.1996

Kerames (CR), 20.3.1993

Anemone coronaria, in an abandoned field near Ayios Pavlos (CR), 1.3.1996

Ophrys fusca Link
ssp. *leucadica* (Renz) H.Kretzschmar
Lefkada Ophrys

Diagnostics: small, squat, delicate plants with up to 5 small to medium-sized flowers, of which the lip, weakly divided into three lobes is either not, or only very slightly, bent downwards at the base. The edges of the lip are turned under and often have a very narrow yellow margin. The basic colour of the lip is dark to black-brown, becoming lighter towards the centre. The central part of the lip is framed by a grey to light-blue "omega" line, coloured silver-blue or rarely intense blue in patches or marbling, becoming reddish-brown towards the grooved base of the lip. Colour and form are very variable, as indicated in the photographs.

Habitat: meadow areas, phrygana, from low-lying areas to above 900 metres.

Hybrids: with *Ophrys cinereophila*, *Ophrys iricolor*.

Confusion: not possible with the other subspecies, since this ssp. is not found on Crete. The Taxon is characterised on Rhodes by numerous local varieties.

Flowering period: middle of II to beginning of IV.

Skafi (KA), 23.3.01

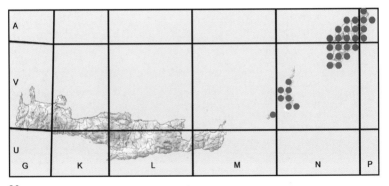

Lastos (KP), 21.3.2001

Lastos (KP), 21.3.2001

Lindos (RH), variant, 28.3.2002

Ophrys fusca Link
ssp. *thriptiensis* (Paulus) H. Kretzschmar
Thripti Ophrys

Diagnostics: very small, less than 10 cms high, squat plants with 1-3 medium-sized flowers. Flowers extremely early, before all the other orchids on the peaks above Thripti. Through the flat weals on the edge of the groove the lip resembles that of ssp. *creberrima*, but has no fold. Silver-grey blazon, grooved base of lip.

Habitat: Thripti massif, in locations above 700 and up to 1400 metres.

Hybrids: not known.

Confusion: hardly possible, given its early flowering period and its very localised area of distribution.

Flowering period: middle of II to end of III.

Remarks: it is difficult to categorise this Taxon, due to the fact that a small peripheral variety from the lower-lying region of pine woodlands, perhaps even influenced hybridogeneously (through ssp. *creticola*), is described here, although the main population of this plant in the high reaches of Afendis exhibits considerable discrepancies to the type described.

Orino (CR), 28.3.96

A					
V					
U					
G	K	L	M	N	P

Biotope south of Thripti in sparse pine forest of *Pinus brutia,* 9.5.1997

Thripti (CR), 5.3.2001, S. HERTEL   Orino (CR), 28.3.1996

Ophrys iricolor DESF.
Rainbow Ophrys

Diagnostics: purple-black, very large lip, covered by a deep dark blue blazon proceeding from the base of the lip. Deep, wide groove at the base of the lip; at its edges the groove has well-defined swollen tracks which are suffused with pinkish-violet to orange brown colour towards the edge of the lip. The underside of the lip exhibits brilliant red "rainbow colours".

Habitat: species typically found in phrygana, in open and well-grazed spaces, where the plants often grow beneath thorny bushes for protection and their flowers peek out of the bush. Sometimes occurring in large clumps as a successional plant, in areas in areas after forest fires.

Hybrids: with *Ophrys fusca* ssp. *leucadica, Ophrys fleischmannii, Ophrys cretica* ssp. *ariadnae, Ophrys mammosa, Ophrys spruneri* ssp. *grigoriana*.

Flowering period: middle of III to middle of IV.

Confusion: hardly possible, given the colour of the underside of the lip and the size of the flow-

Analipsi (CR), 17.4.2003

ers. Only the extremely early flowering *Ophrys mesaritica* bears a similarity; the underside of the lip of its much smaller flowers is green-brown.

Prodromi (CR), 9.4.2000

Gennadio (RH), 14.4.1983

Prodromi (CR), 9.4.2000

Ophrys mesaritica Paulus & C. & A. Alibertis
Mesara Ophrys

Diagnostics: extremely early flowering, slim, tall plant, strongly resembling a very small *Ophrys iricolor*, with the underside of the lip green to greenish-brown. The basic colour of the lip is blackish-purple with a dark blue blazon which is, however, less brilliant in appearance than in *Ophrys iricolor*. The base of the lip, in comparison, bears a deep, wide groove. There is similarity with a Taxon designated *Ophrys astipalea* from the island of Astypalea.

Habitat: in open, grazed land, also in very bushy phrygana. It mainly occurs in the area of the Mesara Plain in southern Crete and in the Asterousia Mountains.

Hybrids: not known.

Flowering period: beginning of I to end of II.

Confusion: hardly possible, in spite of the similarity with the much more widely-distributed *Ophrys iricolor*. The flowering period and the colouration of the underside of the lip are indicative, and the flowers are much smaller than those of *Ophrys iricolor*.

Grigoria (CR), 27.2.1996

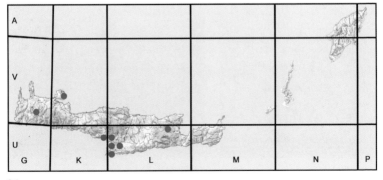

Margaraki (CR), 27.2.1996

Lendas (CR), 1.3.1996

Lendas (CR), 1.3.1996

Ophrys omegaifera H. Fleischm.
ssp. *basilissa* (C. & A.Alibertis & H.R.Reinhard) H.Kretzschmar
Royal Ophrys

Diagnostics: one of the largest flowers in the genus *Ophrys*; the lip can be more than 30 mm in length. The edge of the three-lobed lip is covered with fine, velvety hairs, dark brown. The blazon is bare, of a contrasting, lighter colour, and edged by a wide whitish to blue "omega". The lip- fold is not as strong and is more rounded that in ssp. *omegaifera*, running in an arched fashion over the major part of the lip, thus the lip hangs downwards.

Habitat: meadow areas, grassy phrygana, in open ground, only on basic subsoil.

Hybrids: mixed populations with ssp. *omegaifera* in western Crete.

Confusion: differentiated from *ssp. omegaifera* through the lip-fold, and

Rodovani (CR), 9.4.2000

also because the lip is much longer. The hairs are also distributed differently: in the case of *ssp. omegaifera* they are considerably longer and "more bristly", while in ssp. *basilissa* they are finer and more velvet to the touch.

Flowering period: beginning of II to beginning of IV.

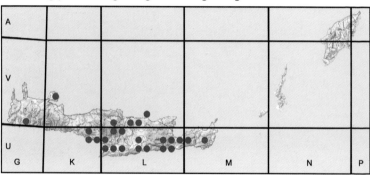

Festos (CR), 26.2.1996

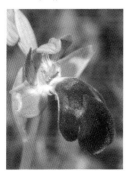

Antiskari (CR), 26.2.1996

Miamou (CR), 26.2.1996

Antiskari (CR), 26.2.1996

99

Ophrys omegaifera H.Fleischm.
ssp. *omegaifera*
Omega Ophrys

Diagnostics: mostly strong plants, not infrequently growing in small clumps. Flowers often stand erect from the stem. Lip has no groove at the base, and is strongly folded only a short distance from it. Up to 20 mm in length, dark brown and with long hairs on the edge. The metallic or red-violet coloured blazon is bare, bordered towards the front by a wide whitish or light blue band. On Karpathos, the plants are mostly considerably more delicate than those on Crete, and their lip is less conspicuously folded.

Habitat: in bushy meadow phrygana, in pine woodland.

Hybrids: with *Ophrys sicula*. Mixed populations with ssp. *basilissa*.

Confusion: possible with Ophrys sitiaca, but the latter has a clear, though flat, groove at the base. The sharp fold in the lip is absent in ssp. *basilissa*, and the lip is much longer.

Flowering period: end of II to middle of IV.

Laerma (RH), 2.4.1995

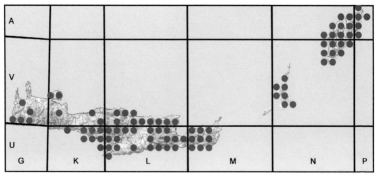

Apollona (RH),25.2.1997

Apella (KP), 20.3.2000

Koutsouras (CR), 5.4.1992

Melambes (CR), 14.4.2000

Ayios Stefanos (CR), 7.4.1993

Ophrys sitiaca Paulus & C. & A.Alibertis
Sitia Ophrys

Diagnostics: medium-sized flowers, lip only slightly folded with a flattish groove at the base. Lip dark brown and velvet haired. Blazon is bare reddish-brown-violet to blue-grey, bordered towards the tip of the lip through a broad, whitish-grey "omega" marking.

Habitat: pine woodland, phrygana. From mid-March onwards flowering plants only found in very shady places.

Hybrids: no definite hybrids known.

Confusion: mainly possible with subspecies of *Ophrys fusca*, but differentiated from them through the shallower groove and the mostly absent fold at the base of the lip. On Crete, where it has been described, the Taxon is rare, only locally more common, while in other places, e.g. on Rhodes, it is common. To date, it has not been found on the other islands in the region.

Flowering time: beginning of II to middle of III.

Laerma (RH), 26.2.2004

Thripti (CR), 5.3.2000, S. Hᴇʀᴛᴇʟ - with Pollinator

Thripti (CR), 5.3.2001, S. Hᴇʀᴛᴇʟ

Laerma (RH), 26.2.2004

Ophrys lucis (KALTEISEN & H.R.REINHARD) PAULUS
Light Ophrys

Diagnostics: mostly small, delicate plants with few flowers which can be highly variable. Outline of lip can be clearly or weakly three lobed, the edges of which can be either lightly or considerably turned backwards; thus it takes many forms. Lip medium brown to black-brown with velvet hair, which is often longer and lighter in colour on the shoulders. The embossed blazon is a metallic bluish colour in the form of two flecks joined in the middle. Sepals pink, sometimes white, rarely green. The long lanceolate petals are darker than the sepals.

Habitat: Clearings in pine or cedar woodlands.

Hybrids: with *Ophrys ferrumequinum, Ophrys reinholdii, Ophrys tenthredinifera.*

Confusion: possible with *Ophrys ferrum-equinum*, although the basic colour of the latter is always a dense black with only short black hairs on the shoulder and no division of the lip.

Flowering period: end of II to beginning of IV.

Kolimbia (RH), 24.2.1997

Kolimbia (RH), 24.2.1997

Kolimbia (RH), 24.2.1997

Laerma (RH), 4.4.1995

Kolimbia (RH), 24.2.1997

Laerma (RH), 4.4.1995

Laerma (RH), 3.4.1995

Ophrys mammosa/sphegodes - group

Ophrys herae

Ophrys mammosa

Ophrys sphegodes
  ssp. *cretensis*
  ssp. *gortynia*

This group of comprises of plants which have an undivided lip and which have more or less pronounced humps on the shoulder of the lip. Therefore these species can relatively easily be confused with one another when the forms deviate slightly from the norm and in addition transitional forms may occur locally.

Ophrys mammosa occurs on Crete, Karpathos and Rhodes, but to date has not been found on Kasos. It's instance is very typical on Rhodes and Karpathos, since the other three related types are not found there. By contrast, plants with sepals coloured an intensive pink are commonly found on Crete; these possibly constitute transitions to *Ophrys spruneri* ssp. *spruneri* (see picture on right). It is also probable that the description of *Ophrys spathiotica* H.Fleischmann (a Taxon which is repeatedly the subject of controversy) actually refers to this plant, which is not rare in south-east Crete. Locally (e.g. in the Asterousia Mountains) there are also larger mixed populations with *Ophrys cretica ssp. ariadnae*. Occasionally, in particular in eastern Crete, there are also plants with long beak-like connective appendages, a characteristic of the eastern Mediterranean *Ophrys transhyrcana*. On Crete, they can be seen as variants within normal populations. *Ophrys mammosa* flowers rather late, definitely after *Ophrys herae* and *Ophrys sphegodes* ssp. *cretensis*.

Gölz & Reinhard (1996) have examined the whole group biometrically. They describe the close relationship of *Ophrys herae* and *Ophrys sphegodes*

Analipsi (CR), 6.4.93 - *Ophrys sphegodes* ssp. *cretensis* (left), ssp. *gortynia* (right)

ssp. *cretensis*, which in western Crete are only separated from each other with difficulty, while in eastern and central Crete their differentiation is much clearer. Both species are early flowering, in low-lying areas from mid-February onwards. The plants designated here as *Ophrys herae* are well-defined morphologically, even if many different populations can be observed. *Ophrys herae* is mostly squat, but thus a stronger plant than *Ophrys sphegodes* ssp. *cretensis* and has fewer, although clearly larger, flowers than the Cretan Spider orchid. The basic colour of the lip in *Ophrys herae* is red-brown; it has mostly strong humps on the lip which are coloured red-brown or yellowish. The flowers of *Ophrys sphegodes* ssp. *cretensis* have only small lips of a basic dark black-brown colour. They are rounded in outline and only seldom have very weak humps at the base.

The name *Ophrys pseudomammosa* RENZ is also used as a synonym for *Ophrys herae*, and describes the hybrid *Ophrys mammosa* x *Ophrys sphegodes* from the Greek mainland.

Ophrys sphegodes ssp. *gortynia* is relatively isolated by its late

Analipsi (CR), 17.4.03 – plants in which the sepals are suffused with colour.

flowering period. Its flowers are much larger than those of ssp. *cretensis*. The lip is conspicuously flat and mostly thinly edged in yellow. There are often humps at the base of the lip. The photograph (below, left) shows the difference quite clearly.

Ophrys sphegodes ssp. *gortynia* is not endemic to Crete. It is attested on Naxos (KRETZSCHMAR 1966) and on other Cycladic islands in large populations. By contrast, reports of *Ophrys sphegodes* ssp. *cretensis* outside Crete seem to be due to confusion with *Ophrys sphegodes* ssp. *gortynia*.

Ophrys herae M.Hirth & H.Spaeth
Hera's Ophrys

Diagnostics: Mostly stocky and strong plants, seldom tall and often found in small groups. Medium-sized lip, smaller than that of *Ophrys mammosa* with which it is often confused because of the strong, frequently lighter-coloured humps. The outline of the lip is rounded, 10-15 mm in diameter. Whitish to blue blazon, H-shaped on the lighter central part of the lip, mostly with an intensively coloured border. Border of the lip brown-black to red-brown, short-haired and velvety, with longer hairs on the very edge of the lip. Sepals green to whitish-green, mostly red on the lower half, petals shorter, dark yellow-green to green-brown.

Habitat: meadow phrygana, slopes, common in western Crete, rarer in central and eastern Crete, also on acid subsoil.

Prodromi (CR), 9.4.2000

Hybrids: mixed populations with *Ophrys sphegodes* ssp. *cretensis* are common in western Crete.

Confusion: with the other Taxa of the group.

Flowering period: End of II - middle of IV.

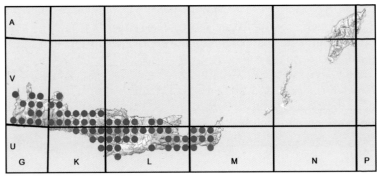

108

Kerames (CR), 2.3.1996

Azogires (CR), 9.4.2000

Kerames (CR), 2.3.1996

Rodovani (CR), 9.4.2001

Ophrys mammosa DESF.
Breasted Ophrys

Diagnostics: multiflowered, often tall plant. Basic colour of the lip blackish red-brown, velvet-haired, undivided, with strong lateral humps coloured red towards the middle of the lip. Edges of the lip turn downwards, very strongly, in which case the outline of the lip is triangular. Lateral sepals in the lower half are suffused with red. Spatula-shaped petals, shorter than the sepals. The connective appendage is occasionally long-beaked, a characteristic of *Ophrys transhyrcana* which has a distribution much further east. Populations influenced by *Ophrys spuneri* are not infrequent on Crete, while the species is very stable on Karpathos.

Habitat: phrygana, in open spaces. Widely distributed, mostly small populations, on basic soil.

Hybrids: with *Ophrys cretica* ssp. *ariadnae* and ssp. *cretica*, *Ophrys sphegodes* ssp. *gortynia* and *Ophrys spruneri* ssp. *spruneri*, *Ophrys iricolor*.

Confusion: with other species in the group.

Flowering period: end of III - end of IV.

Apella (KP), 21.3.2000

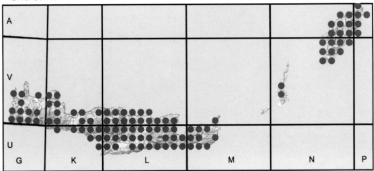

Apella (KP), 28.3.1998

Analipsi (CR),17.4.2003

Messangros (RH), 14.4.1983

Analipsi (CR),17.4.2003

Analipsi (CR),17.4.2003

Ophrys sphegodes MILL.
ssp. *cretensis* H.BAUMANN & KÜNKELE
Small Cretan Spider Ophrys

Diagnostics: multiflowered, tall plant, often growing in groups. Lip small, rounded in outline, less that 10 mm in diameter. The blazon is H-shaped on a slightly lighter centre section of the lip, the edge of the lip is brown-black to black, with short velvety hairs. Sepals green to whitish-green, petals somewhat shorter, darker yellow-green.

Habitat: phrygana, remains of pine forests, slopes, to 1300 metres.

Hybrids: with *Ophrys cretica* ssp. *ariadnae, Ophrys herae, Ophrys tenthredinifera.*

Confusion: distinguished from ssp. *gortynia* and *Ophrys mammosa* through its flowering period and very different size of lip. The latter has, in addition, a much flatter lip, often with a yellow border. Differentiation from *Ophrys herae*, with which it blends locally in western Crete, is more difficult. The flowers of *Ophrys herae* are larger, the basic colour of the lip is a reddish brown, and the lips practically always have strong humps.

Flowering period: middle of III to middle of IV.

Ay. Varvara (CR), 27.3.94

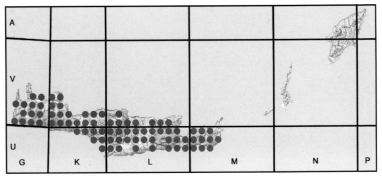

Orino (CR), 10.4.1993

Ziros (CR), 6.4.1993

Orino (CR), 9.4.1993

Vatos (CR), 13.4.2000

Thripti (CR), 10.4.1994

Ophrys sphegodes MILL.
ssp. *gortynia* H.BAUMANN &KÜNKELE
Gortys Ophrys

Diagnostics: undivided lip, mostly with small humps. Elongated outline, not rounded as in ssp. *cretensis*, lip over 12 mm long. Basic colour black to black-brown, velvet-haired, edge of lip often has a yellow border and normally stands out flat to the side, not (or very weakly) curled. The blazon is H-shaped. As a rule, the plants are delicate, with fewer flowers than ssp. *cretensis*, late flowering, absent from the west of Crete.

Habitat: phrygana, dry meadows, open olive groves, in open spaces, typically in relatively low-lying areas, on basic soil.

Hybrids: with *Ophrys cretica* ssp. *cretica, Ophrys mammosa*.

Confusion: differentiation from ssp. *cretensis* has already been described in detail there. From the point of view of the flowering period, it can only be found together with *Ophrys mammosa*, from which it is distinguished through the flat, often yellow edges of the lip and the sepals, which have hardly any colour.

Flowering period: Middle of IV - beginning of V.

Analipsi (CR),17.4.2003

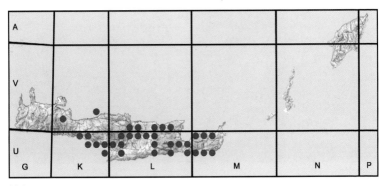

Analipsi (CR), 17.4.2003

Saktouria (CR), 13.4.2001

Goudouras (CR), 11.4.1994

Meseleri (CR), 12.4.1994

115

A note about some of the *Ophrys* species

Ophrys phryganae and *Ophrys sicula* together constitute the most commonly-found of all the *Ophrys species*. In the Aegean, there are some regions in which these two species approach each other considerably in appearance, while in others, notably on Crete, they are clearly distinguishable from one another. The convergence mentioned here is especially connected with the diameter of the lip, which in *Ophrys phryganae* in particular almost corresponds to that of *Ophrys lutea* from the western Mediterranean area. There are, however, not infrequent instances of populations where the dimension of the lip approximates that of *Ophrys sicula*. On the other hand, large-lipped specimens of *Ophrys sicula* are also found. In spite of this the two Taxa remain clearly distinguishable through their differing appearance and the form of the lip, even though the variation in the size of the lip may present problems of differentiation. The lip of *Ophrys phryganae* is

Extensive, old olive cultivation at Festos (CR), 25.3.00

Dry meadow biotope south of Ayios Isidoros (RH), 25.3.00

clearly bent downwards at the base, while that of *Ophrys sicula* is straight at the base.

The dark middle part of the lip of *Ophrys phryganae* is, with its bluish mirror in the upper part, equally strongly arched downwards, while the edge of the lip turns upwards again. The bluish mirror area is warty in the area of the fold. The lip is less arched in *Ophrys sicula* and the warts at the base of the lip are absent.

Ophrys lucis and *Ophrys aegeae* can also be seen as closely related; at first they were viewed as variants of the central Greek *Ophrys argolica*, and later as two subspecies of the separate category of *Ophrys aegeae*. They are well differentiated morphologically, and completely separated from a geographical point of view. *Ophrys aegeae* was long viewed as endemic to Karpathos, but also occurs, for example, on Amorgos. *Ophrys ferrum-equinum* is closely related to *Ophrys aegeae* and *Ophrys lucis*; thus it is not surprising that hybrids with this species are often found, and intermixtures occur locally.

Two more closely-related species are *Ophrys regis-ferdinandii* and *Ophrys speculum*. They are particular inhabitants of dry areas, which are frequently found in the interior of Rhodes and along the gravel margins of the river beds. The picture above shows one such typical area in the hilly zone of the island interior. Both species are commonly found on Rhodes, not infrequently together. They are nevertheless easy to differentiate. Hybrids do occur, but only rarely in larger numbers.

Ophrys phryganae J. & P.Devillers-Terschuren
Phrygana Ophrys

Diagnostics: relatively strong, mostly squat plants. The flowers stand almost horizontally away from the stem and each bloom consecutively at almost 90 degrees to the other.The sepals are green and the petals yellow-green; in comparison with *Ophrys sicula* they are both more widely open. The lip is folded downwards at the base. A rather stately blazon in dark brown, metallic, bluish and sometimes intense blue in the centre. Wide, strong yellow three-lobed edge of the lip, which first bends downwards but then turns up again right at the very edge. The width of the lip can be more than 12mm but occasionally smaller. On the fold, the base of the lip rises up in wart-like fashion at it's transition to the edges of the stigmatic cavity.

Ayios Isidoros (RH), 4.4.95

Flowering period: end of III to end of IV.

Habitat: meadow areas, often in small groups, in areas which have been strongly grazed, in open spaces, frequently as a successional plant. The species is common on all of the islands.

Hybrids: rare with *Ophrys sicula*.

Confusion: with *Ophrys sicula*, but differentiated for example by the lip fold.

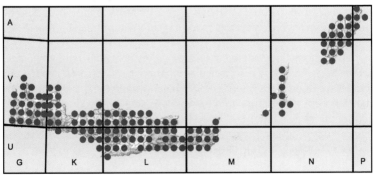

Margaraki (CR), 13.4.1994

Kattavia (RH), 28.3.2002

Kattavia (RH), 28.3.2000

Apollona (RH),18.3. 2002

119

Ophrys regis-ferdinandii (Renz) Buttler
King Ferdinand's Ophrys

Diagnostics: Flowers small and insect-like in appearance. Three-lobed lip, middle lobe with the lateral margins turned strongly backwards, edges with long orange-brown to dark brown hairs, surface bare and brilliant blue to dark-violet in colour. Lateral lobes mostly greenish-yellow, with long hairs on the edges. Stigmatic cavity black, glossy and chitin-like, with two marked "pseudo-eyes". Petals red to red-violet, turned backwards, the middle sepalum standing up towards the front over the stigmatic cavity, side sepals green, reddish-violet in the lower half, in addition often blue-speckled. The flowers open consecutively, thus strong plants can reach heights of over 30 cms.

Habitat: phrygana, always in open spaces, with a particular preference for extremely dry, gravel areas.

Hybrids: with *Ophrys mammosa* and *Ophrys speculum*.

Confusion: hardly possible.

Flowering period: beginning of III to beginning of IV.

Lachania (RH),19.3.2002

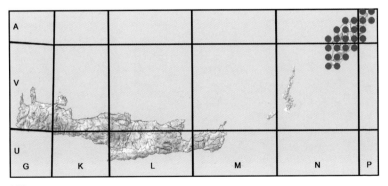

120

Plimiri (RH), 19.3.2002

Apolakkia (RH), 23.3.2000

Plimiri (RH), 29.3.2000

Kattavia (RH), 29.3.2002

121

Ophrys reinholdii H. FLEISCHM.
Reinhold's Ophrys

Diagnostics: relatively large flowers, lip always three-lobed, lateral lobes long and strong, and mostly covered in light-coloured to almost white hairs, with small humps. Middle lobe deep black in colour, velvet-haired, wider towards its protuberance, edge of the middle lobe mostly turned upwards. Blazon embossed from the base, forming a white band or framing white edged, glossy metallic, bluish or red-violet areas. Sepals greenish-white to pinkish-red with a green central vein, petals spatula-shaped, about half as long as the sepals, darker brownish to strongly reddish in colour. Stigmatic cavity white inside with a dark horizontal line, sometimes also suffused with blue.

Habitat: pine woodlands, areas re-cultivated after forest fires, logging sites, in sparse shade.

Hybrids: with *Ophrys cretica*, *Ophrys ferrum-equinum* and *Ophrys lucis*.

Confusion: hardly possible.

Flowering period: end of III to end of IV.

Apolakkia (RH), 26.3.2000

Istrios (RH), 5.4.1995

Istrios (RH), 5.4.1995

Laerma (RH), 10.4.1993

Istrios (RH), 5.4.1995

Istrios (RH), 5.4.1995

Istrios (RH), 5.4.1995

Ophrys sicula TINEO
Small Yellow Ophrys

Diagnostics: delicate plant with a thin stem, which is greatly extended at flowering, especially in vigorous examples. Diameter of the lip normally less than 10 mm, edge light yellow, mostly narrower than in *Ophrys phryganae*. Blazon similar, but the lip is not folded at the base and arches downwards in its entirety. Edge only a little bent backwards. Side borders of the groove without warty swellings. Blazon mostly metallic shining, rarely coloured intense blue.

Habitat: little-demanding plant, phrygana, remains of pine forests, meadow areas, ruderal places, open olive groves.

Hybrids: with *Ophrys phryganae, Ophrys omegaifera* ssp. *omegaifera*.

Confusion: with *Ophrys phryganae*. A problem is presented by the fact that in the Aegean region instances of conspicuously large-flowered *Ophrys sicula* occasionally occur as well as extremely small-flowered *Ophrys phryganae*, but the characteristics of the lip form are retained.

Flowering period: II-IV, in several waves.

Lahania (RH), 28.3.2000

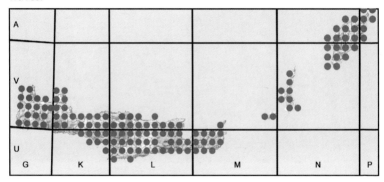

Fri (KA), 22.3.2001

Eleousa (RH),20.4.1983

Fri (KA),22.3.2001

Ophrys speculum LINK
Mirror Ophrys

Diagnostics: Lip clearly three-lo-bed, lateral lobes flat and pointing upwards, bare on the top and on the side towards the lip, long black or more rarely dark-brown hairs on the edges as well as on the middle lobe, which is only lightly arched, bare on the surface, intensive blue to dark blue in colour, the blue area often also with a thin yellow or orange edge. The middle sepal stands over the pistil column, the side sepals are intensive violet to brown-violet striped in the lower half, sometimes also with violet dots. The stigmatic cavity is chi-tin-like and black in colour, petals turned backwards.

Habitat: phrygana, dry meadows, river gravel, open spaces, rarely in forests. Instable outside Rhodes.

Hybrids: with *Ophrys ferrum-equi-num, Ophrys regis-ferdinandii.*

Confusion: hardly possible, on account of its unique colouring.

Flowering period: beginning of II to middle of III.

Asklippio (RH), 18.3.2002

Kattavia (RH), 28.3.2000

Asklippio (RH), 26.2.1997

Plimiri (RH), 18.3.2002

Asklippio (RH), 18.3.2002

Plimiri (RH), 18.3.2002

127

Ophrys spruneri NYMAN
ssp. *grigoriana* (G. & H. KRETZSCHMAR) H. KRETZSCHMAR
Grigorian Ophrys

Diagnostics: colouring similar to that of the ancestral Taxon, however the blazon is practically always framed in whitish-blue to sky blue. Very large flowers. Lip without fully formed lateral lobes, only with light indentations in its outline. Lip about one and a half times as long as the middle sepals. Stigmatic cavity correspondingly forms a wide, horizontally-orientated oval, white in the upper part, but below a black horizontal line with an intensive sky blue area between two likewise sky-blue bordered "eye" areas.

Habitat: meadows, grassy phrygana, meadowy slopes, terraces.

Hybrids: with *Ophrys cretica* ssp. *ariadnae, Ophrys iricolor.*

Confusion: possible with early flowering ssp. *spruneri,* although at similar altitudes this has certainly finished flowering when ssp. *grigoriana* begins to flower.

Flowering period: from beginning to end of IV.

Remarks: endemic to Crete, certainly more widely distributed than apparent to date.

Grigoria (CR), 12.4.2003

Grigoria (CR), 12.4.2003

Grigoria (CR), 12.4.2003

Grigoria (CR), 12.4.2003

Grigoria (CR), 12.4.2003

Ophrys spruneri NYMAN
ssp. *spruneri*
Spruner's Ophrys

Diagnostics: strong plants with stately flowers. Pink sepals, in the lower section often somewhat darker at the sides, petals shorter and narrower, pinkish red to red-greenish. Lip deeply divided into three lobes with a larger middle lobe, about as long or slightly shorter than the middle sepalum, with a small, reddish-coloured forward pointing protuberance at the tip. Base colour deep velvet black, blazon grey-blue to intensive blue, proceeding in an H-shape from the base of the lip and extending out to the lower half of the stigmatic cavity, bordered by a blue horizontal line towards the pistil column and ending in 2 blue or black pseudo-eyes. Border of the blazon sometimes coloured an intense blue.

Habitat: meadow areas, grassy phrygana, open olive groves.

Hybrids: with *Ophrys bombyliflora, Ophrys cretica* ssp. *ariadnae, Ophrys episcopalis, Ophrys mammosa, Ophrys sphegodes* ssp. *gortynia, Ophrys tenthredinifera.*

Confusion: with ssp. *grigoriana*, which only has a suggestion of a divided lip, and flowers later.

Flowering period: middle of II to beginning of IV.

Ay. Galini (CR), 1.3.1996

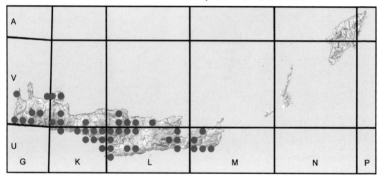

Akoumia (CR), 27.2.1996

Ay. Galini (CR), 1.3.1996

Gero Kambos (CR), 26.2.1996

Ay. Kirillos (CR), 6.4.1994

Ophrys tenthredinifera WILLD.
Wasp Ophrys

Diagnostics: mostly squat plants, commonly in groups. Undivided lip, forming mostly only flattish humps at the sides, thickly haired. Basic colour mostly yellow, more rarely yellow-brown, enclosing a black-brown area, covered with short-hairs, in the middle. Blazon bare, enclosing an orange basal field towards the top, and developing downwards into a mostly whitish-framed, metallic-shining mirror. Stigmatic cavity dark and wide. Column short and blunt-ended. Pink sepals, more rarely white, round-ended. Petals short, thickly haired, darker than the sepals.

Habitat: meadowy phrygana, terraced fields, pine woodland, common on Crete.

Hybrids: with *Ophrys bombyliflora, Ophrys episcopalis, Ophrys heldreichii, Ophrys lucis, Ophrys sphegodes* ssp. *cretensis, Ophrys spruneri* ssp. *spruneri.*

Confusion: hardly possible.

Flowering period: beginning of III to end of IV, but from the beginning of II on Rhodes.

Messeleri (CR), 12.4.1994

Spoa (KP), 21.3.2000

Kolimbia (RH), 25.2.1997

Skafi (KA), 22.3.2001

Ay. Ioannis (CR), 14.4.2003

Ophrys umbilicata DESF.
ssp. *rhodia* H.BAUMANN & KÜNKELE
Rhodian Umbilical Ophrys

Diagnostics: sepals and petals green, middle sepal turned backwards and not standing over the pistil column. Lip strongly three-lobed, lateral lobes ending in short horns, thickly haired at the base. Blazon of white lines encloses an orange basal field and frames a metallic blue area below it. The species is endemic to the southern Aegean.

Habitat: meadow areas, grassy phrygana, dry meadows.

Hybrids: with *Ophrys bombyliflora, Ophrys dodekanensis, Ophrys episcopalis, Ophrys heldreichii, Ophrys oestrifera*.

Confusion: with *Ophrys oestrifera* and with *Ophrys umbilicata ssp. umbilicata*, from both of which it is differentiated by its constantly green sepals and petals, and from the latter species in addition by its middle sepal, which is always turned backwards, and through the form of the lip.

Flowering period: beginning of IV to middle of V.

Lardos (RH), 29.3.2002

Platania (RH), 11.4.1995

Lardos (RH), 29.3.2002

Ay. Isidoros (RH),12.5.1997

Ophrys umbilicata DESF.
ssp. *umbilicata*
Umbilical Ophrys

Diagnostics: sepals and petals whitish to pink, more rarely green, middle sepal thrown forwards over the pistil column, while the petals are turned backwards. Lip strongly three-lobed. Lateral lobes ending in short, pointed horns, and thickly haired at the base. The blazon of white lines encloses an orange-brown basal field and below it frames a reddish-violet metallic area. The middle lobe of the lip widens towards the tip. The distribution of this species radiates only into the south-eastern Aegean; it mainly occurs much further eastwards.

Habitat: meadow areas, dry meadows.

Hybrids: with *Ophrys candica*, *Ophrys oestrifera*.

Confusion: with ssp. *rhodia*, but the position of the middle sepal is different.

Flowering period: end of III to end of IV.

Kattavia (RH), 28.3.2000

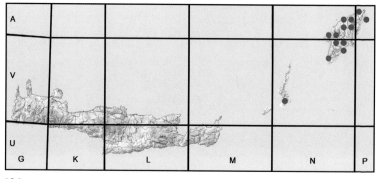

Kattavia (RH), 28.3.2000

Akramitis (RH), 27.3.2000

Ayios Isidoros (RH), 7.4.1995

137

Orchis anatolica - Group

The species of this group which occur in the region are very closely related to one another. Genetic research carried out by Bateman (2001: 119) established the number of different

Orchis anatolica - quadripunctata:	9
Orchis anatolica - sitiaca:	12
Orchis quadripunctata - sitiaca:	15

Overview of the base-pair difference between the species of the group

base-pairs in a particular section of DNA (the so-called ITS segment). Only very minimal differences were found here, as is shown in the overview above. For comparison, according to the same source the number would be 21 in the case of the species pair *Orchis militaris - purpurea* which are considered to be especially closely related. This close relationship has led to the formation of complex hybrid-swarms in eastern Crete, which totally combine the fertile hybrids of both parents with each other; this results in totally introgressive hybridization, with the absorption of one or both parent parts in the hybrid swarm.

Orchis quadripunctata is certainly strictly dependent on basic subsoils; *Orchis sitiaca* typically grows on superficially acid areas. Inasmuch as *Orchis anatolica* occurs in typical form on Crete, it is found on basic soil, while a definite preference cannot be identified for the species in other locations. On Rhodes, Kasos and Karpathos, where *Orchis quadripunctata* is not found, *Orchis anatolica* occurs in very typical form, mostly in very stony areas, both on basic as well as on acid subsoil. In eastern Crete *Orchis anatolica* occurs alongside the hybrid swarms mentioned above, but *Orchis quadripuncta-ta* has been completely eclipsed in them. Here, in suitable areas, the somewhat later flowering *Orchis sitiaca* is a rare addition. The hybrid species has been designated in the eastern Mediterranean as *Orchis sezikiana* (pro. hybr.) by B. & H. Baumann. However, since especially in the case of the heterogeneity of the plants of eastern Crete there are differences to those in the Turkish and Cypriot populations, this Taxon is not included in the present book.

Orino (CR), 10.5.97 – Orchis anatolica x Orchis quadripunctata from eastern Crete

Orchis quadripunctata, Kato-Saktouria (CR) 14.4.2003

Orchis anatolica Boiss.
Anatolian Orchid

Diagnostics: large flowers, loosely arranged, coloured white to red, middle part of the lip bears dark red dotted lines. Long spur, directed upwards, becoming thin towards the tip. Stem suffused with intense red towards the top. Light green leaves, regularly spotted.

Habitat: stony cliffs, patchy phrygana, in open spaces, also on acid soil.

Hybrids: with *Orchis pauciflora*, *Orchis prisca*, hybrid swarms with *Orchis quadripunctata*.

Confusion: with *Orchis sitiaca*, which has a looser inflorescence and silver-green leaves.

Flowering period: end of III to middle of IV

Remarks: finds on Rhodes, Karpathos and Kasos are undoubtedly to be identified as *Orchis anatolica*. By contrast, older observations reported from Crete are often doubtful, because *Orchis sitiaca* had not been differentiated. In eastern Crete, for example, along with hybrid swarms with *Orchis quadripunctata* there are small numbers of plants to be found which are surely to be designated *Orchis anatolica*.

Ay. Mamas (KA), 22.3.2001

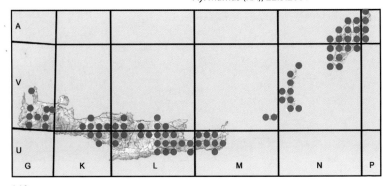

Ay. Isidoros (RH), 13.3.2002

Ay. Isidoros (RH), 13.3.2002

Volada (KP), 2.4.1998

Orino (CR), 14.4.1992

Orchis quadripunctata Cirillo ex Ten.
Four-spotted Orchid

Diagnostics: unmistakable in its typical form. The flowers are mostly small, coloured red to white (particularly frequent in populations at altitudes above 1200 metres). Sepals and petals of the same colour, lip weakly to clearly three-lobed, all lobes almost of the same size. Entrance of spur mostly light coloured; the dark red spots which give the plant its name are also located here. Front part of the lip without spots. Very thin spur, ending thread-like, horizontal or directed downwards. Intense green leaves, with black spots.

Habitat: altitudes up to 1300 metres and above, stony areas, on stony slopes, in rock clefts, only on basic subsoils, often together with *Orchis pauciflora*.

Flowering period: end of III to middle of V.

Melambes (CR), 12.4.1992

Hybrids: with *Orchis pauciflora* and *Orchis sitiaca*, hybrid swarms with *Orchis anatolica*.

Confusion: the thin, downward-directed spur and the small lip with three equally large lobes can serve to differentiate clearly from all the other species of the group.

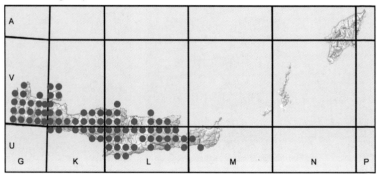

Melambes (CR), 2.4.1994 - Ridge of Bouvala

Kamares (CR), 10.4.1992

Saktouria (CR), 29.3.1994

Orchis sitiaca (Renz) Delforge
Sitia Orchid

Diagnostics: mostly loose inflorescence with large blooms. Spur particularly large and strong, markedly bent upwards at the end and becoming thinner, but blunt-tipped. Strong division of the lip, lateral lobes turning downwards, which makes it appear narrow when viewed from above; two parallel lines of dark red dots in the lighter coloured, often rather yellowish middle part. Inside of the sepals intensively striped in green. Very characteristic foliage, of a conspicuous green colour suffused with grey-silver, with only fine, dark spots.

Vatos (CR), 20.4.1993

Habitat: meadow areas, particularly on soils tending to superficial acidity (e.g. on serpentine, in meadowy phrygana), to altitudes of 1300 metres and above.

Flowering period: beginning of IV to beginning of V.

Hybrids: with *Orchis pauciflora, Orchis provincialis, Orchis quadripunctata*.

Confusion: occasionally possible with *Orchis anatolica*, but can be readily differentiated through its foliage.

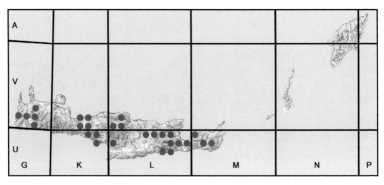

Vatos (CR), 14.4.2003

Vatos (CR), 14.4.2003

Vatos (CR), 14.4.2003

Orchis boryi RCHB.f.
Borys Orchid

Diagnostics: flowers in sequence from bottom to top of inflorescence, otherwise reminiscent of *Orchis morio*. Inside of sepals greenish striped. Lip rounded, mostly only a suggestion of division into side lobes, darker in colour at the edges than in the centre, where there are several irregular dark red-violet flecks. Basic colour of lip dark red-violet, rarely pink or white. Leaves of the foliage without spots, upper part of stem suffused with red. Plants around 20 cms, but sometimes also up to 40 cms in height.

Habitat: areas tending towards superficial acidity with a meadow-like character, often together with *Orchis sitiaca*. Absent on Rhodes, Kasos and Karpathos.

Flowering period: beginning of IV to V.

Hybrids: rarely with *Orchis*

Vatos (CR), 13.4.2000

laxiflora, often with *Orchis papilionacea* ssp. *heroica*.

Confusion: hardly possible on account of the sequence of opening of the flowers, otherwise similar to *Orchis morio*, which is not found on Crete. Not infrequently found growing together with *Orchis laxiflora*, from which it is differentiated by the thinner, downward-pointing spur.

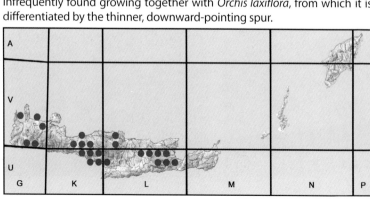

Ay. Ioannis (CR), 4.4.1993

Vatos (CR), 13.4.2000

Vatos (CR), 14.4.2003

Orchis collina Banks & Sol. ex Russell
Hill Orchid

Diagnostics: light green, slightly glossy, unspotted leaves, flowers greenish-white to dark pinkish-red. Lip rounded, undivided, mostly with a darker marking in the middle, short, thick, sac-like spur.

Habitat: phrygana, meadow areas, dry meadows, in open spaces.

Hybrids: Jahn & Schönfelder (1995) mention a hybrid with *Serapias lingua*.

Confusion: hardly possible, as it is the only *Orchis* with a sac-like spur.

Flowering period: I-II, middle of III to beginning of IV.

Remarks: while often rare elsewhere, this is one of the most common species on Crete, particularly at altitudes of between 400 and 800 metres. It flowers in two phases; the delicate plants have already finished flowering in areas near the coast by the end of February, but the main flowering period begins from the middle of March (thus practically without a break) and mostly features conspicuously robust plants. It is relatively common in the southern part of Rhodes, but only one find, long uncorroborated, has been reported from Karpathos.

Kattavia (RH), 14.3.2000

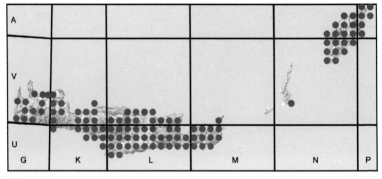

Melambes (CR), 12.4.1992

Saktouria (CR), 12.4.1992

Melambes (CR), 14.3.2003

Saktouria (CR), 29.3.1994

Orchis fragrans Pollini
Bug Orchid

Diagnostics: the perigonal leaves form a helmet which is pointed towards the front. Spur thick and bent lightly downwards. Lip frequently bent backwards towards the spur. Dark spots on lip, basic colour light greenish to dark red-brown, very variable. Plants mostly delicate, up to 30 cms in height, often growing in groups.

Habitat: in areas that have been well-grazed, phrygana, on occasionally damp, basic soils, to a height of 1200 metres.

Hybrids: with *Anacamptis pyramidalis* and *Orchis sancta*.

Confusion: with *Orchis sancta*, which however has larger, unspeckled flowers with wider lateral lobes. It is difficult to differentiate the leaf rosette from that of *Anacamptis pyramidalis*.

Flowering period: beginning of IV to the end of V.

Remarks: some reports which have contributed to the distribution map are only based on the finds of rosettes, thus confusion with *Anacamptis pyramidalis* is possible. The illustration (bottom right) is worthy of note: it shows pollination being carried out by a huge wasp.

Yerakari (CR), 17.5.01

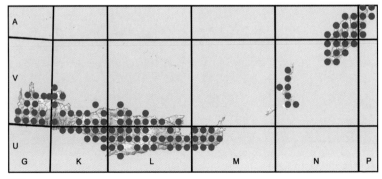

Zaros (CR), 16.05.2001

Ay. Forokli(KP), 29.3.2001

Kalathos (RH), 12.5.1997

Kerames (CR), 17.5.2001

151

Orchis italica Poir.
Italian Orchid

Diagnostics: with mostly dark spotted rosette leaves typically undulate at the edges. The spike is ball-like to ovoid in shape, sepals and petals forming a helmet slightly open towards the front. Lip three-lobed, the middle lobe is divided again into three at the tip, the side tips are narrow, sometimes very narrow, wedge-shaped and ending in sharp points.

Habitat: common species, often in large clumps, in meadowy phrygana, also in sparse pine woods, on basic soils to an altitude of 900 metres.

Hybrids: attested with *Aceras anthropophorum* on Crete and Karpathos, questionable with *Orchis simia*, although it is often found together with the latter.

Apella (KP), 29.3.2001

Confusion: with *Orchis simia*, in which the tips of the lip are mostly coloured a deep red, do not become narrower but remain the same width until the tip, which is rounded. Particularly characteristic of *Orchis italica* are the undulate, speckled leaves, which in *Orchis simia* are wide, oval, smooth-edged and unspeckled.

Flowering period: End of III to the end of IV.

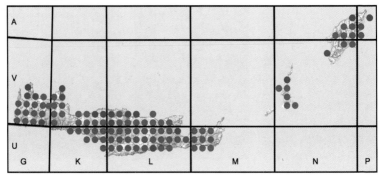

152

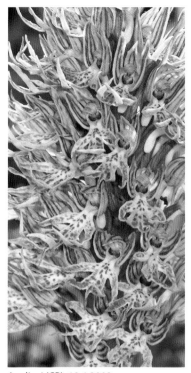

Analipsi (CR), 18.4.2003

Ay. Isidoros (RH), 6.4.1995

Apella (KP), 29.3.2001

Mournies (CR), 11.4.2001

Orchis lactea POIR.
Milky Orchid

Diagnostics: small, but mostly robust plants, inflorescence ball-like to ovoid in shape. Helmet of flowers closed, the tips only minimally spreading out. Basic colour of the lip is mostly yellowish-white, lip three-lobed with a wide middle lobe, only a suggestion of division at the tip, wide lateral lobes standing out to the side. Inside of perigonal leaves green-striped. Strong spur, pointing downwards, about the length of the ovary.

Habitat: grassy places in phrygana, meadow areas, only on basic subsoils. The plant is quite common on Crete, very rare on Karpathos and not found on Kasos. It's occurrence on Rhodes is limited to the north of the island.

Confusion: with *Orchis tridentata*, in which the helmet formed by the sepals is wider open. In addition the tips of the sepals in *Orchis tridentata* are more extended and all the lip lobes end in several sharp, fringe-like points.

Hybrids: with *Orchis tridentata*.

Flowering period: end of II to beginning of IV.

Yerakari (CR), 13.4.03

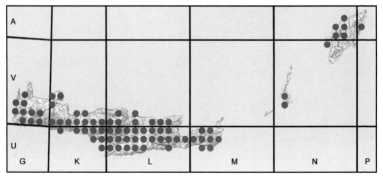

154

Apollona (RH), 26.2.1997

Akoumia (CR), 10.4.1992

Vatos (CR), 9.4.1994

Vatos (CR), 14.4.2003

Yerakari (CR), 13.4.2003

155

Orchis laxiflora Lᴀᴍ.
Lax-flowered Orchid

Diagnostics: strong, stately plants, reaching to over 50 cms in height. Leaves stiffly pointing upwards, rilled. Colour of flower deep red-violet, only the centre of the lip contrasting in white, and this white area sometimes finely spotted. Lip pulled in at the tip, sides turned under towards the back. Large spur, pointing upwards. Occasionally alternative colouration is found, with pink or white blooms.

Habitat: dependent upon wet biotopes, such as damp meadows, edges of streams, areas where there are springs in terraced terrain, also in coastal marshes affected by salt, e.g. near Frangokastello. Only in open areas and on basic subsoils. The occurrence of the species has been strongly reduced due to human activity.

Hybrids: with *Orchis boryi*, *Orchis morio* and *Orchis papilionacea*.

Confusion: *Orchis boryi* has similarly-coloured flowers but the plants are smaller, their spur is shorter and orientated horizontally to downwards.

Flowering period: beginning to end of IV.

Spili (CR), 13.4.2000

156

Apella (KP), 29.3.2001

Spili (CR), 14.4.2003

Spili (CR), 14.4.2003

Lardos (RH), 6.4.1995

Orchis morio L.
ssp. *picta* LOISEL.
Small Orchid, Green winged Orchid

Diagnostics: delicate plant with unspeckled leaves and loose inflorescence consisting mostly of only a few flowers. Inside of helmet green-striped. Lip weakly three-lobed, lateral lobes turned backwards, dark red-violet, mostly dark-spotted in its whitish coloured middle section, seldom without spots. Spur about as long as the ovary, pointing straight or only very slightly upwards.

Habitat: found on Rhodes in meadowy clearings in pine woodlands. Not found on Crete, where it is replaced by *Orchis boryi*. There are two reports, long uncorroborated, of finds on Karpathos.

Hybrids: with *Orchis laxiflora* and *Orchis papilionacea*.

Confusion: possible with *Orchis laxiflora* or *Orchis boryi*. However, *Orchis laxiflora* has an unspotted lip, and its rilled leaves stand vertically on the stem. *Orchis boryi* flowers on the spike from top to bottom, and in addition is not found on Crete.

Flowering period: end of III to end of IV.

Profitis Ilias (RH), 30.3.02

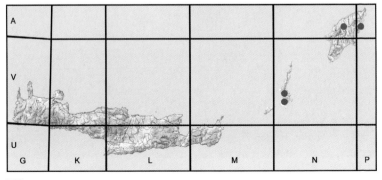

Profitis Ilias (RH), 28.3.2002

Profitis Ilias (RH), 28.3.2002

Profitis Ilias (RH), 28.3.2002

Profitis Ilias (RH), 30.3.2002

Orchis palustris Jacq.
Marsh Orchid

Diagnostics: strong plants, up to more than 90 cms in height. Stiffly erect leaves, rilled and pointing upwards. Flowers pink to red-violet with lighter-coloured centre part of lip, lateral lobes of lip not turned over but flattened with small, protruding middle lobe. Spur shorter in length than the ovary, directed slightly upwards. The Cretan plants intermediate between var. *robusta* T.STEPHENSON and ssp. *elegans* HEUFFEL. Their flowers are smaller than those of the parent species as it is found for example in Central Europe, but the inflorescences are much richer in blooms.

Habitat: coastal marshes, occurrence greatly reduced owing to human activity. Of the spots where it has previously been found, only one is still valid to date, but even this is seriously endangered owing to the progress of tourist development.

Hybrids: none known on Crete.

Confusion: *Orchis laxiflora* is slightly more delicate, the flowers are much darker in colour with a long, upward-pointing spur.

Flowering period: middle of IV to middle of V.

Malia (CR), 14.4.2001

Malia (CR), 14.4.2001

Malia (CR), 9.4.2001

Malia (CR), 14.4.2001

Orchis papilionacea L.
ssp. *alibertis* G. & H. KRETZSCHMAR
Alibertis' Butterfly Orchid

Diagnostics: tall, lanky plant with few flowers, in its appearance resembling a very slim *Orchis papilionacea* ssp. *rubra*. Lip of the flower clearly smaller than in *Orchis papilionacea* ssp. *heroica*, around 10 mm in diameter, edge of lip directed upwards, thus the lip is spade-like. Basic colour of lip white, with red-violet lines of dots and dashes radiating from the base of the lip to the edge. Perigonal leaves bend relatively close together over the pistil column. Basic colour of sepals an intense dark pink, with red-violet stripes running through them. Number of flowers on the spike minimal. Leaf rosette already withered by the time of flowering.

Habitat: dry meadow areas, phrygana, open olive groves on a basic subsoil.

Hybrids: none known.

Confusion: occasionally with the early flowering *Orchis papilionacea* ssp. *heroica*, but clearly differentiated by its appearance and size of flowers.

Flowering period: middle of IV to beginning of V.

Ay. Yannis (CR), 18.4.00

Ay. Yannis (CR), 18.4.00

Miamou (CR), 15.4.00

Remarks:

Probably has a considerably wider distribution, but earlier the subspecies was not differentiated from ssp. *heroica*.

Miamou (CR), 15.4.00

Orchis papilionacea L.
ssp. *heroica* (E.D.CLARKE) H.BAUMANN
Heroic Butterfly Orchid

Diagnostics: low-growing, strong plants with a mostly ball-like inflorescence. Sepals and petals darker than the lip, dark-red striped, forming a loose, open helmet. Lip undivided, often undulate at the edge, basic colour in all shades from white to pink, dark red striped, diameter reaching to over 20 mm. Strong spur, pointing downwards, about the same length as the ovary. As a rule, the leaf rosette is still completely green at the time of flowering.

Habitat: phrygana, dry meadows, in open spaces, also in sparse pine woodland, only on basic subsoils.

Hybrids: with *Orchis boryi* and *Orchis laxiflora*.

Plimiri (RH), 17.3.2002

Confusion: only possible with *Orchis papilionacea* ssp. *alibertis*, but differentiated through its appearance and larger, numerous flowers.

Flowering period: beginning of II to beginning of IV.

Remarks: Because this orchid favours well grazed areas it tends to have it's shoots eaten, thus encouraging a tendency towards a bushy type plant where this occurs.

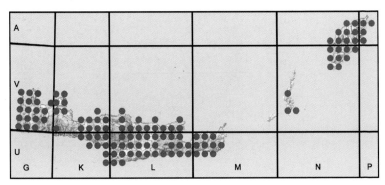

Kerames (CR), 20.4.1993

Apollona (RH), 13.3.2002

Plimiri (RH), 29.3.2000

Plimiri (RH), 27.3.2002

Festos (CR), 26.2.1996

Orchis pauciflora Ten.
Sparsely-flowering Orchid

Diagnostics: mostly small plants with few flowers and unspeckled rosette leaves. Flowers are two different shades of yellow: the lip is a darker, intense yellow, and the remaining perigonal leaves are light yellow. The flowers are very large with long, strong spurs that turn upwards. Only slight indication of a division of the lip into three lobes, with the sides folded downwards, but when viewed from the side either no rounding or a rounding that has been flattened is visible, with fine red dots in the middle. In fresh flowers the spur entrance is often an intense green.

Habitat: rocky areas, edges of precipices, more rarely also in grassy phrygana, mostly in open spaces, also in forest/woodland clearings. Only on basic subsoils, at altitudes of 1300 metres and above, whereby the flowering period is quite extended.

Hybrids: with *Orchis quadripunctata*, *Orchis sitiaca*.

Confusion: with *Orchis provincialis*, which has smaller, much lighter flowers; it's rosette leaves are flecked with intense black.

Flowering period: middle of III to beginning of V.

Melambes (CR), 14.4.2003

Yerakari (CR), 14.4.2003

Melambes (CR), 1.4.1994

Prodromi (CR), 9.4.2000

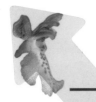

Orchis prisca HAUTZ.
Cretan Orchid

Diagnostics: plant of the mountain regions. Glossy, unspeckled leaves, flower-bearing stem strongly suffused with red. Flowers have a short spur, only about half as long as the ovary. Lateral sepals intense green in the centre, often with dark red dots, the edges pinkish-red, standing out to the side. Middle sepalum and petals bend together over the pistil column and form a helmet. Lip pink with a lighter centre, with dark red dots, three-lobed, the lateral lobes turning downwards.

Habitat: sparse pine woodland, bushy phrygana, particularly common above detritus-filled gulleys, on basic subsoils above 800 metres.

Hybrids: with *Orchis anatolica*.

Confusion: only with the hybrid mentioned, which mostly also bears the green markings in the sepals, although they are less emphasised. The length of the spur is a decisive criterion here; in hybrids it is considerably more than half the length of the ovary.

Flowering period: End of IV to the end of V.

Orino (CR), 8.5.1997

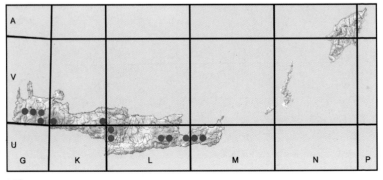

168

Thripti (CR), 9.5.1997

Thripti (CR), 9.5.1997

South-west slope of Afendis, Thripti (CR), 17.5.01. Biotope with *Orchis prisca*.

Orchis provincialis Bᴀʟʙ. ex Lᴀᴍ. & DC.

Provence Orchid

Diagnostics: leaves of the rosette speckled in intense black. Flowers light yellow, only centre of lip darker yellow. Strong, long spur bent upwards, lip slightly three-lobed. Lateral lobes strongly turned under. Seen from the side, the lip appears rounded and curves strongly downwards (sheep's nose), with fine red dots in the middle which in individual cases appear to join up with one another.

Habitat: bushy phrygana, in open spaces, also in thin woodlands of Q. pubescens in western Crete, only on acid subsoils, at altitudes from 600 to 1400 metres.

Hybrids: with *Orchis anatolica* and *Orchis sitiaca*.

Confusion: the rosette with its speckled leaves and the light yellow colour of the flowers make this species unmistakable, and thus distinguishable from the large-flowered *Orchis pauciflora* and the yellow-flowered *Dactylorhiza romana*.

Flowering period: end of III to end of IV.

Vatos (CR), 14.4.2003

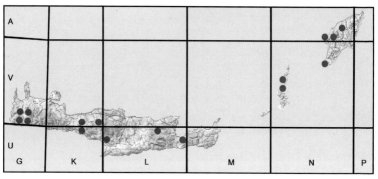

Biotope on Prof. Ilias (RH), 29.3.2002

Prof. Ilias (RH), 29.3.2002

Vatos (CR), 9.4.2001

Orchis punctulata STEVEN **ex** LINDL.
Spotted Orchid

Diagnostics: tall plants, growing to over 40 cms in height, with large, strong, unspeckled leaves. Helmet closed, yellow, inside of sepals striped with red-brown. Lip an intense yellow to red-brown with a yellow centre, bearing reddish clumps of hair, three-lobed, middle lobe widening at the end and divided again into three; a small protuberance sits between these lobes.

Habitat: phrygana, in open spaces, commonly beneath and within thorn bushes.

Hybrids: not known.

Confusion: unmistakable in the flowering state because of its colour and form. After finds were made to the west of Epta Piges and north of Profitis Ilias the species vanished for a long time, but was rediscovered again in the south of Rhodes in 1986. Given the fact that numerous potential biotopes exist, more finds are certainly expected. The photographs were taken in southern Cyprus.

Flowering period (estimated): II to III.

Limassol (Cyprus), 10.2.95

Limassol (Cyprus), 10.2.95

A						
V						
U						
G	K	L	M	N		P

Limassol (Cyprus), 10.2.1995

Diagnostics: closely related to *Orchis fragrans*, but the flowers are considerably larger. At the time of flowering, the leaves have almost always withered. Flowers pink-red to white, lip unspotted. Thick spur, thinner at the end, pointing downwards, mostly bent forwards. Lip three-lobed, lateral lobes with clear hollows at the edge. Sepals and petals form a closed helmet which ends in a sharp, extended point.

Habitat: bushy phrygana, in open spaces, dry meadows.

Hybrids: with *Orchis fragrans*.

Confusion: with *Orchis fragrans*, particularly as a rosette, when no differentiation is possible. Hybrids are very common and are easy to identify from the flowers, which are larger than those of *Orchis fragrans*, and from the speckles which are to be found on the lip of the latter.

Remarks: rare on Crete and Karpathos, only found in a few places near the coast. By contrast, it is very common on Rhodes.

Flowering period: end of IV to end of V.

Istrios (RH), 5.5.1997

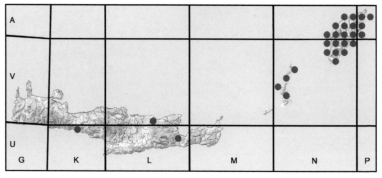

Vati (RH), 12.5.1997

Vati (RH), 12.5.1997

Istrios (RH), 5.5.1997

175

Orchis simia LAM.
Monkey Orchid

Diagnostics: stately plant with a strong rosette of glossy leaves. Lip three-lobed at base, middle lobe divided again into two with all four tongues thus created, about the same in appearance and retaining their width to the tip, mostly dark red in colour. Helmet bears delicate pink stripes inside, includes all sepals and petals. Very characteristic order of flowering, from the top to the bottom of the inflorescence.

Habitat: terraced fields, in bushy phrygana, in pine woodland.

Hybrids: attested with *Aceras anthropophorum* on Crete and Karpathos. Questionably with *Orchis italica*.

Confusion: with *Orchis italica*, which has leaves with an undulating edge and flower tips which become progressively narrower towards the front.

Flowering period: end of III to end of IV.

Remarks: occurs on Crete locally in large populations. This is normally a species found at altitudes of around 600-800 metres, where it is able to flower relatively late. It is a conspicuously squat plant on Karpathos, and rare on Rhodes.

Mournies (CR), 12.4.2001

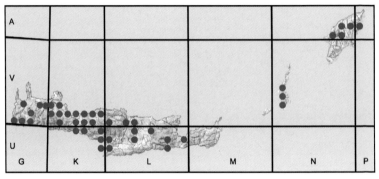

176

Rodovani (CR), 9.4.2000

Vatos (CR), 10.4.1993

Tsiskiana (CR), 9.4.2001

Apella (KP), 28.3.2001

Mournies (CR), 12.4.2001

Orchis tridentata Scop.
Three-toothed Orchid

Diagnostics: slim, delicate plants of higher regions. Usually with few flowers, loosely arranged, often conspicuously directed to one side. The helmet formed by the sepals is not closed, but slightly open at the tip, so that the extended tips project away from each other like three teeth – hence its name. Basic colour of lip light pink to white, decorated with a dark violet pattern of lines and dots. Lip three-lobed in outline, the larger middle lobe ending at the tip again in two small lobes. In addition, all of the ends of the lip have a sharply drawn-out tip.

Habitat: mostly in the shade of thorny phrygana bushes as protection in areas which are subject to extensive grazing. Only on basic subsoils, to an altitude in excess of 1300mts.

Hybrids: only with *Orchis lactea*.

Confusion: with *Orchis lactea*, which has a closed helmet and more flowers arranged in a thicker spike, the edges of the lips of the flowers not ending in a sharp tongue.

Flowering period: Middle of IV to the middle of V.

Imbros Pass (CR), 12.4.00

Imbros Pass (CR), 12.4.2000

Yerakari (CR), 12.4.2001

Yerakari (CR), 12.4.2001

Katharo (CR), 9.5.1997

179

The Genus Serapias

Genetically, this genus is comparatively close to that of *Anacamptis*. This may be the reason why occasionally hybrids between species of the two genera have been observed. Within the genus *Serapias* the genetic differences are very small.

The variability of all the species is high; thus for example *Serapias bergonii*, one of the most common, tends to exhibit variations in the size of its flowers. They may be extremely small, so that such plants have hitherto often been reported as *Serapias parviflora*. The distribution map for this species thus surely includes a large number of false determinations of small-flowered *Serapias bergonii* in relatively dry spots. For this reason, the picture on the right particularly shows such delicate, squat plants which clearly do not belong to *Serapias parviflora*.

The autogamous nature of *Serapias parviflora* is the reason why even plants which are just beginning to flower already have strongly swollen ovaries. This makes the species unmistakable.

Two other species are relatively isolated from the ecological point of view because of their reliance on mainly acid subsoils; these are *Serapias lingua* and *Serapias cordigera* ssp. *cretica*, between which hybrids are not rare occurrences. Perhaps the very great variability of *Serapias cordigera* ssp. *cretica* on Crete, which leads to considerable deviations from the main species, should be seen as the result of introgression from *Serapias lingua*.

Biotope with *Serapias bergonii* near Margaraki (CR), 14.4.03

Festos (CR), 19.4.00

Festos (CR), 19.4.00

Festos (CR), 19.4.00

The fifth type, *Serapias orientalis*, is well isolated. In contrast to the other varieties it is more tolerant of dry conditions and flowers earlier.

The nominate Taxon manifests itself via a large spectrum in the colour of the flowers, while ssp. *carica* is quite uniformly dark reddish-violet in colour and has smaller flowers.

All allogamous species are pollinated by bees, which spend the cold nights inside the flower-sheaths because the temperature is several degrees higher there than outside. Pollinia are thereby acquired and transferred. Several bees can be found simultaneously within a single flower.

Serapias bergonii E.G.Camus
Bergoni's Serapias

Diagnostics: Leaf rosette of narrow, rilled leaves, enclosing the lower part of the flower stem. Stem of the plant suffused with red-violet above the leaves. Flowers arranged on the stem at an angle and one above the other, with a brown-violet bract emanating from the base of each ovary, the former as a rule clearly longer than the individual flower. The rear part of the brown-violet lip forms a tube with the closely arranged sepals and petals, out of which the front part of the lip projects forwards and downwards.

Habitat: in open spaces, meadows, ditches, prefers places which are intermittently damp. Grows on basic and slightly acid subsoil.

Hybrids: with *Serapias lingua* and *Serapias orientalis*.

Confusion: extreme variation in the size of the flowers. Specimens with small flowers are always being confused with *Serapias parviflora*, although the allogamous nature of *Serapias bergonii* permits a clear differentiation.

Flowering period: Beginning of IV to the end of V.

Kamilari (CR), 11.4.01

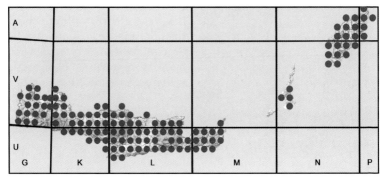

Analipsi (CR),18.4.2003

Kalathos (RH), 28.3.2002

Grigoria (CR), 15.4.2003

Grigoria (CR), 15.4.2000

183

Serapias cordigera L.
ssp. *cretica* B. & H. BAUMANN
Heart-flowered Serapias, Cretan subspecies

Diagnostics: the fine, dark red shading on the lower section of the stem is a characteristic feature found in no other *Serapias* species. A few, upright leaves enclose the stem at the bottom in a sheath-like manner. The flowers are almost as large as those of *Serapias orientalis*. Typical of the plant, and that which gives it its name, is the heart-shaped front part of the lip, which can range from narrow to wide. The helmet, formed from sepals and petals and contrastingly coloured a lighter, reddish-light grey, is also characteristic. The lip is dark black to reddish-brown, very rarely lighter in colour, and has long, brush-like hairs in the middle section.

Habitat: only on acid subsoil, in bushy phrygana, particularly in undergrowth consisting of *Sarcopoterium spinosum*.

Hybrids: with *Serapias lingua*.

Confusion: with hybrids between *Serapias cordigera* and *Serapias lingua*, which have only a single, furrowed swelling.

Flowering period: end of IV to end of V.

Sisarha (CR), 9.5.01

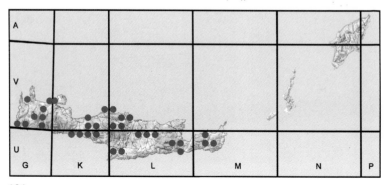

Sisarha (CR), 9.5.2001

Mournies (CR), 17.5.2001

Sisarha (CR), 9.5.2001

Astiraki (CR), 9.5.2001

Serapias lingua L.
Tongue Serapias

Diagnostics: occasionally very small, delicate plants of only 10 cms in height, but also vigorous plants, sometimes more than 40 cms in height, often in very dense populations. Mostly a suggestion of a rough two-rowed arrangement of the leaves, which fold upwards at the middle. Colour of lip light pink to intense red, sometimes also yellow, lateral lobes of the back part of the lip an intense darker colour. The simple, dark red weals at the base of the lip are characteristic; all other species have two parallel swellings.

Habitat: meadows, gulleys which are intermittently damp, damp places among phrygana, as a successional plant, on acid subsoils or subsoils at least tending towards acidity. Locally common, but very sporadically distributed.

Hybrids: with *Serapias bergonii, Serapias cordigera* ssp. *cretica.*

Confusion: unmistakable in view of the characteristic swelling at the base of the lip. Hybrids with *Serapias bergonii* are sometimes difficult to differentiate.

Flowering period: Beginning of IV to the end of IV.

Dris (CR), 10.4.01

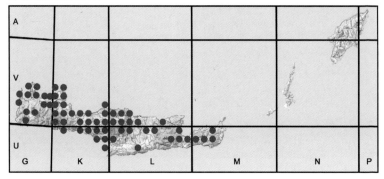

Dris (CR), 10.4.2001

Plemeniana (CR), 10.4.2001

Akrotiri-Chania (CR), 21.4.1992

Serapias orientalis (GREUTER) H. BAUMANN & KÜNKELE
ssp. *carica* H.BAUMANN & KÜNKELE
Eastern Serapias, South-West Anatolian subspecies

Diagnostics: plants resemble *ssp. orientalis*. Allogamous, large flowers, lip between 2 cms and 5cms in length, deep dark brown-violet, front part pointed, inverted ovoid in shape, with long hairs in the area of the fold. Stem suffused with violet.

Habitat: represents the species on Rhodes, but the somewhat larger-flowered main species is not found there. Centre of distribution in the south, in meadowy areas on soil which is alternately damp and dry, thin phrygana.

Hybrids: difficult to identify, mixed populations with *Serapias bergonii*.

Confusion: with the other *Serapias* species, but differentiated immediately through the size of the flowers. The bracts in this mainly squatter and stronger variety are only as long as the flowers.

Flowering period: end of III to end of IV.

Remarks: As with all other allogamous Serapias varieties, this subspecies is also pollinated by the small wild bees which sleep inside the flowers (see right).

Plimiri (RH), 29.3.2002

Plimiri (RH), 29.3.2002

Pollinator, Kattavia (RH), 29.3.02

Plimiri (RH), 29.3.2002

Kattavia (RH), 29.3.2002

Serapias orientalis (Greuter) H.Baumann & Künkele
ssp. *orientalis*
Eastern Serapias, common subspecies

Diagnostics: form of the plant and colour of the flowers incredibly variable; on dry subsoils it remains squat, but on damper subsoils has a longer extended stem. Flowers large, lip up to more than 5 cms long (larger and longer extended than in the ssp. *carica*), ranging from deep dark brown-violet to completely greenish-white in colour. Helmet formed from sepals and petals commonly contrasts in colour to the lip. Front part of the lip pointed, inverted ovoid in shape, with long hairs particularly in the area of the fold. Lateral lobes projecting out to the sides, coloured darker than the rest of the lip, protruding out of the sheath.

Habitat: meadow areas, on land which is intermittently damp, alluvial land, in full sun, on basic

Ierapetra (CR), 19.4.2003

soil. Particularly common locally on Karpathos, more common in the east than in the west of Crete, found up to an altitude of 800 metres.

Hybrids: with *Serapias bergonii*.

Confusion: with the other *Serapias* species, but differentiated clearly by the size of the flowers. The leaves do not reach higher than the the flowers in this stocky, strong variety. The lateral lobes of the lip standing well out of the sheath are an unmistakable characteristic.

Flowering period: end of III to end of IV.

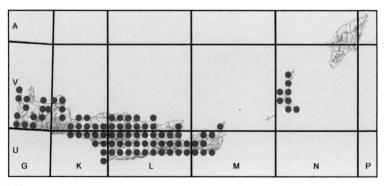

Apella (KP), 29.3.2001

Apella (KP), 29.3.2001

Kamilari (CR), 14.4.2000

Ay. Marinas (KP),29.3.2001

Kamilari (CR), 7.4.1993

Serapias parviflora PARL.
Small-flowered Serapias

Diagnostics: an autogamous species, the flowers of which already exhibit a clearly thickened, swollen ovary in the bud or opening stage. The parts of the lip which project from the helmet are very small, under 10 mm in length, and mostly strongly bent backwards. Colour of the lip light brown to sometimes almost yellowish-white. Helmet consisting of sepals and petals coloured brownish-grey, lateral lobes of the back part of the lip completely hidden in this sheath. In contrast to the small flowers and sparsely-flowered short spikes the leaves are very long and almost reach to the lower end of the inflorescence.

Habitat: meadow areas on marshland which is acidic or influenced by the presence of salt, on areas which are alternately dry and damp.

Hybrids: not known.

Confusion: its autogamous nature differentiates it from all other Serapias species.

Flowering period: beginning of IV to middle of V.

Remarks: Probably over-represented in the distribution map, due to confusion with *Serapias bergonii*.

Malia (CR), 15.4.2003

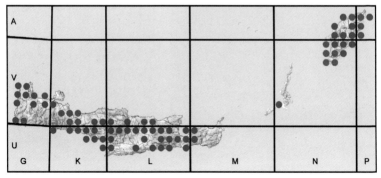

Sternes (CR), 21.4.1992

Kattavia (RH), 5.4.1995

Kattavia (RH), 5.4.1995

Malia (CR), 15.4.2003

Spiranthes spiralis (L.) CHEVALL.
Autumn Lady's Tresses

Diagnostics: delicate plant with small, white flowers in long, twisted spikes, with the lip coloured green at the base. Flowering stem grey-green, covered with felt-like whitish hairs. During the flowering period a new rosette forms at the base, next to the flowering stem, and this grows after the flowering, during the winter and spring. The very characteristic rosettes of dark-green leaves with their fatty gloss can be seen at the time of flowering of most other species of orchid in spring.

Habitat: on superficially acid damp places in phrygana, in open spaces, in thin pine woodland, and in sheep folds.

Hybrids: none known.

Confusion: unmistakable, especially the rosettes of dark-green leaves with their fatty gloss.

Flowering period: middle of X to end of XI.

Remarks: Certainly more common in occurrence than shown in the distribution maps, since the rosettes often go unnoticed.

Mournies(CR), 26.10.2001

Prof. Ilias (RH), 30.3.2002

Ay. Mamas (KP), 23.3.2001

Mournies (CR), 27.10.2001

Sporadic occurrences and questionable species

Orchis pinetorum Boiss. & Kotschy from Rhodes, *Ophrys melena* (Renz) Paulus & Gack, *Cephalanthera damasonium* (Mill.) Druce, *Cephalanthera rubra* (L.) Rich.and *Epipogium aphyllum* Sw. have been reported sporadically from Crete. "The spots where these species are supposed to be found are shown on the map below.

Krasi (CR), 8.4.1994

Konitsa (GR), 14.5.2003

Germany, 6.7.03

Germany, 6.7.03

Dadia (northern Greece), 10.5.03

Hybrids

The southern Aegean islands are distinguished by a very large number of different hybrids, in particular within the genus *Ophrys*.

A whole series of the hybridisations presented here has not been described to date. In addition several other mixed forms are mentioned, although they certainly only constitute extreme variations of one of the parents mentioned. A detailed description cannot be provided in this book because of the limitations of space. Nevertheless, an illustration of all the hybrids definitely found in this region can at the very least be included, in alphabetical order according to the hybrid formula. More extensive information on the subject can be found in KRETZSCHMAR & al. (2001, 2002).

Aceras anthropophorum × *Orchis italica*

Apella (KP), 28.3.2001

Aceras anthropophorum × *Orchis simia*

Menetes (KP), 27.3.2001

Anacamptis pyramidalis × *Orchis fragrans*

Lardos (RH), 12.4.1995

Epipactis cretica × Epipactis microphylla

Zaros (CR), 2.6.1999, C. Kreutz

Ophrys aegaea × Ophrys cretica ssp. ariadnae

Diafani (KP), 12.3.2001, S. Hertel

Ophrys aegaea × Ophrys ferrum-equinum

Diafani (KP), 12.3.2001, S. Hertel

Ophrys blitopertha × Ophrys cinereophila

Gennadio (RH), 31.3.1995

Ophrys bombyliflora × Ophrys cretica ssp. ariadnae

Ay. Ioannis (CR), 5.4.1994

Ophrys bombyliflora × Ophrys heldreichii

Ay. Ioannis (CR), 16.4.2003

Ophrys bombyliflora × Ophrys umbilicata ssp. rhodia

Malona (RH), 17.4.1983

Ophrys bombyliflora × Ophrys spruneri ssp. spruneri

Rhodovani (CR), 1984, H. BLATT

Ophrys bombyliflora ×
Ophrys tenthredinifera

Kandila (CR), 18.03.2001, S. Hertel

Ophrys candica ×
Ophrys dodekanensis

Laerma (RH), 26.2.1997

Ophrys candica ×
Ophrys episcopalis

Drimiskos (CR), 17.5.2001

Ophrys candica ×
Ophrys heldreichii

Larani (CR), 31.3.1994

Ophrys candica × **Ophrys oestrifera**	**Ophrys candica × Ophrys** **umbilicata ssp. umbilicata**

Ay. Isidoros (RH), 2.4.1995   Ay. Isidoros (RH), 1.4.1995

Ophrys cinereophila × **Ophrys fusca ssp. creberrima**	**Ophrys cinereophila ×** **Ophrys fusca ssp. leucadica**

Ay. Galini (CR), 27.2.1996   Lastos (KP), 26.3.2001

Ophrys cretica ssp. *ariadnae* × *Ophrys cretica* ssp. *cretica*

Ay. Galini (CR), 14.4.2003

Ophrys cretica ssp. *ariadnae* × *Ophrys ferrum-equinum*

Arkasa (KP), 19.3.2001

Ophrys cretica ssp. *ariadnae* × *Ophrys fusca* ssp. *creberrima*

Ay. Varvara (CR), 9.4.1989, C. KREUTZ

Ophrys cretica ssp. *ariadnae* × *Ophrys heldreichii*

Ay. Varvara (CR), 27.3.1994

Ophrys cretica ssp. ariadnae × Ophrys iricolor

Ay. Ioannis (CR), 12.4.2003, H. BAUMGARTNER

Ophrys cretica ssp. ariadnae × Ophrys mammosa

Antiskari (CR), 3. 4.1994

Ophrys cretica ssp. ariadnae × Ophrys phryganae

Sitia (CR), 8.4.1994 - R. KOHLMÜLLER

Ophrys cretica ssp. ariadnae × Ophrys sphegodes ssp. cretensis

Vistagi (CR), 18.4.2000

Ophrys cretica ssp. *ariadnae* × *Ophrys spruneri* ssp. *spruneri*

Melambes (CR), 14.4.2000

Ophrys cretica ssp. *ariadnae* × *Ophrys spruneri* ssp. *grigoriana*

Margaraki (CR), 3.4.1994

Ophrys cretica ssp. *beloniae* × *Ophrys mammosa*

Kattavia (RH), 14.4.1983

Ophrys cretica ssp. *beloniae* × *Ophrys reinholdii*

Mesanagros (RH), 31.3.1995

Ophrys cretica ssp. *bicornuta* × *Ophrys sphegodes* ssp. *gortynia*

Ferma (CR), 12.4.1994

Ophrys cretica ssp. *cretica* × *Ophrys heldreichii*

Ay. Galini (CR), 14.4.2003

Ophrys cretica ssp. *cretica* × *Ophrys mammosa*

Plora (CR), 9.4.2000

Ophrys cretica ssp. *cretica* × *Ophrys sphegodes* ssp. *gortynia*

Ierapetra (CR),19.4.2003

Ophrys dodekanensis ×
Ophrys episcopalis

Prof. Ilias (RH), 29.3.2002

Ophrys dodekanensis ×
Ophrys oestrifera

Kattavia (RH), 29.3.2000

Ophrys dodekanensis ×
Ophrys umbilicata ssp. rhodia

Prof. Ilias (RH), 15.4.1983

Ophrys episcopalis ×
Ophrys ferrum-equinum

Menetes (KP), 28.3.2001

Ophrys episcopalis × *Ophrys heldreichii*

Grigoria (CR), 3.4.1994

Ophrys episcopalis × *Ophrys umbilicata* ssp. *rhodia*

Eleousa (RH), 19.4.1983

Ophrys episcopalis × *Ophrys spruneri* ssp. *spruneri*

Drimiskos (CR), 7.4.1994

Ophrys episcopalis × *Ophrys tenthredinifera*

Saktouria (CR), 4.4.1992

Ophrys ferrum-equinum × *Ophrys heldreichii*

Kyra Panayia (KP), 5.4.1998

Ophrys ferrum-equinum × *Ophrys lucis*

Kolimbia (RH), 13.3.2000

Ophrys ferrum-equinum × *Ophrys mammosa*

Mesanagros (RH), 12.4.1983

Ophrys ferrum-equinum × *Ophrys reinholdii*

Mesangros (RH), 7.4.1995

Ophrys ferrum-equinum × Ophrys speculum

Mesangros (RH), 18.3.2002

Ophrys fleischmannii × Ophrys iricolor

Ay. Triada (CR), 1.4.1992

Ophrys fleischmannii × Ophrys omegaifera ssp. omegaifera

Orino (CR), 10.4.1994

Ophrys fusca ssp. creberrima × Ophrys fusca ssp. creticola

Ardaktos (CR), 2.3.1996

209

Ophrys fusca ssp. leucadica × **Ophrys iricolor**	**Ophrys heldreichii ×** **Ophrys umbilicata ssp. rhodia**

Arkasa (KP), 19.3.2000   Lardos (RH), 20.3.2002

Ophrys heldreichii × **Ophrys tenthredinifera**	**Ophrys iricolor ×** **Ophrys mammosa**

Saktouria (CR), 7.4.1994   Faliraki (RH), 10.4.1976, W. KREY

Ophrys iricolor ×
Ophrys spruneri ssp. *grigoriana*

Grigoria (CR), 14.4.2003

Ophrys lucis ×
Ophrys reinholdii

Kolimbia (RH), 13.3.2000

Ophrys lucis ×
Ophrys tenthredinifera

Kolimbia (RH), 25.2.1997

Ophrys mammosa ×
Ophrys regis-ferdinandii

SW-Turkey, 8.4.1982, H. Baumann

Ophrys mammosa × *Ophrys sphegodes* ssp. *gortynia*

Plora (CR), 20.4.2000

Ophrys mammosa × *Ophrys spruneri* ssp. *spruneri*

Afrati (CR), 10.4.1994

Ophrys oestrifera × *Ophrys umbilicata* ssp. *rhodia*

Lardos (RH), 4.4.1995

Ophrys oestrifera × *Ophrys umbilicata* ssp. *umbilicata*

Kattavia (RH), 28.3.2000

Ophrys omegaifera ssp. *omegaifera* × *Ophrys sicula*

Arkasa (KP), 18.3.2000

Ophrys phryganae × *Ophrys sicula*

Mournies (CR), 22.4.2000

Ophrys regis-ferdinandii × *Ophrys speculum*

Lahania (RH), 25.3.2000

Ophrys sphegodes ssp. *cretensis* × *Ophrys tenthredinifera*

Drimiskos (CR), 6.4.1994

**Ophrys sphegodes ssp. gortynia ×
Ophrys spruneri ssp. spruneri**

Plora (CR), 20.4.2000

**Ophrys spruneri ssp. spruneri ×
Ophrys tenthredinifera**

Antiskari (CR), 2.3.1995

**Orchis anatolica ×
Orchis prisca**

Orino (CR), 9.5.1997

**Orchis anatolica ×
Orchis provincialis**

Prof. Ilias (RH), 11.4.1983

Orchis anatolica × Orchis quadripunctata

Orino (CR), 3.4.1994

Orchis boryi × Orchis laxiflora

Drimiskos (CR), 15.4.2001

Orchis boryi × Orchis papilionacea ssp. heroica

Drimiskos (CR), 6.4.2000

Orchis fragrans × Orchis sancta

Lardos (RH), 15.5.1997

Orchis italica ×
Orchis simia (?)

Rhodovani (CR), 9.4.00 – questionable!

Orchis lactea ×
Orchis tridentata

Yerakari (CR), 13.4.00

Orchis laxiflora ×
Orchis morio

Prof. Ilias (RH), 11.4.1983

Orchis laxiflora ×
Orchis papilionacea ssp. *heroica*

Prof. Ilias (RH), 11.4.1983

Orchis morio ssp. picta ×
Orchis papilionacea ssp. heroica

Prof. Ilias (RH), 30.3.2002

Orchis pauciflora ×
Orchis quadripunctata

Saktouria (CR), 11.4.1994

Orchis pauciflora ×
Orchis sitiaca

Mournies (CR), 14.4.2000

Orchis provincialis ×
Orchis sitiaca

Vatos (CR), 13.4.2000

Orchis quadripunctata ×
Orchis sitiaca

Melambes (CR), 12.4.1994

Serapias bergonii ×
Serapias lingua

Ay. Galini (CR), 16.4.2000

Serapias bergonii ×
Serapias orientalis

Analipsi (CR), 6.4.1993

Serapias cordigera ×
Serapias lingua

Astiraki (CR), 9.5.2001

Recommended Excursions

With nature lovers who want to get to know the orchid flora of the Mediterranean in mind, we describe a number of excursions here on which most of the species occuring and widely distributed in the region can be found without too much effort. The 'orchid specialist' can also make use of the excursions suggested, since areas are described which lie off the beaten track. We mention a total of 20 excursions; the numbers on the map correspond to those in this chapter.

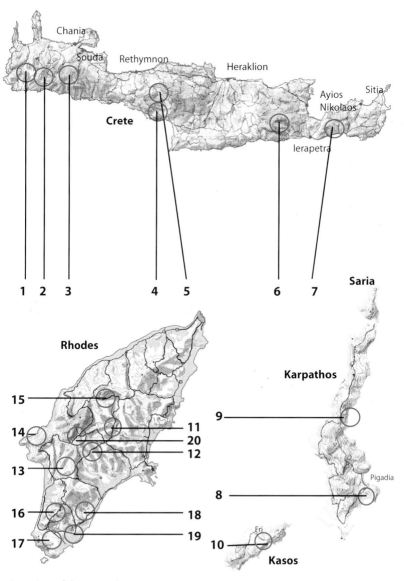

Location of the excursion areas

It should basically be kept in mind that owing to the specific conditions which prevail in the southern Aegean, it is not possible to make absolutely definite recommendations. Change of land use can also lead to the rapid destruction of rich localised populations of plants.

Even in such cases it will normally be possible in the immediate vicinity of a listed Orchid spot, to find a plant of the species concerned in other nearby similar biotopes. The UTM values given are intended primarily for users of GPS direction-finding equipment. They are not measured "to the exact metre", as this would not be of value for the reasons just given.

If you are not only occasionally on the look-out for orchids, but even dedicate a whole holiday to the purpose, then accommodation should be sought in one place and used as a point of departure. In the case of a stay in the early part of the year (end of February to mid-March), the nights can be extremely chilly and it is essential to find accommodation with heating – this is something which is mostly lacking in tourist accommodation of the usual kind. In addition, it will be almost a necessity to rent a car for longer excursions. Areas which have retained their original character will naturally be off the main roads, and this should be taken into account when a vehicle is selected.

It is impossible to recommend a visiting time for the southern Aegean where 'the orchids' are concerned. The flowering periods of the various species are so varied that it is not possible to find every species in flower during a normal sojourn lasting two to three weeks. Most of the species will be found in flower between the months of March and May.

At this juncture a few observations about the technique of photography are appropriate. The photographs in this book were taken using various types of photographic equipment. Until 2000 most of the photographs were taken in medium format (6 x 6) using a Rollei 6008 camera with dia-phragm-shutter lenses. During the same period a Nikon camera was used for photographs in small format. All systems used a speed of at least 1/250s, which is often essential for sharp photographs to avoid a longer exposure time. A digital camera was used for the first time in 2001 and mostly dur-ing 2002, but from 2003 onwards, only a digital single lens reflex camera (Canon) was used.

In conventional photography, sharp pictures in the macro-field are only achieved with the use of a flash in unsuitable weather conditions. If thereby a purely frontal flash is dominant, the picture will be in focus but appear very unnatural with dark, often black background, as can be seen in a number of books. To avoid this, the use of several flash atttachments is basically recommended, in order to light the foreground and background in a natural way. The much better picture achieved by the digital system, particularly with a higher ASA setting, makes it possible to reduce the use of the flash, which is thus advantageous in that it provides much more natural lighting.

1. Crete – the area around Kandanos and Voutas

In this area, hotels are most likely to be found in Paleohora. From there it is a drive of 16 kms to Kandanos; about 3 kms before the village a side road leads off in a westerly direction towards Strovles. Behind Plemeniana the road leads through lowland riparian forest/woodland with small meadowy areas where there are springs. The valley opens out before Drys and meadowy hills can be seen to the north of the road (UTM: **GE 41.62/63**):

Ophrys sphegodes ssp. *cretensis*	*Orchis laxiflora*
Orchis collina	*Serapias lingua* (huge occurrence)

Proceed on to Strovles. Immediately to the west of the village the road runs parallel to a stream, the banks of which are covered in sparse lowland riparian forest/woodland (UTM: **GE 41.27**):

Anacamptis pyramidalis	*Epipactis microphylla*

From Strovles a road leads to the village of Voutas, situated to the south, 16 kms away. A new gravel road to the new hotel complexes on the coast begins here (and will probably soon be asphalted). At the turning to the village of Hatzis (a little field path) there are, below the gravel road and at a distance of about 1 km, wonderful meadowy areas with large populations of many species (UTM: **GE 30.87**):

Anacamptis pyramidalis	*Ophrys phryganae*
Ophrys bombyliflora	*Ophrys sicula*
Ophrys herae	*Ophrys spruneri* ssp. *grigoriana*
Ophrys iricolor	*Orchis italica*
Ophrys omegaifera ssp. *omegaifera*	*Orchis papilionacea* ssp. *heroica*

A little further along this way:

Orchis pauciflora	*Orchis collina*

Paleohora can be reached again along the coastal road, in an easterly direction.

2. Crete – the area around Rodovani

Areas of acid soil are commonly found in western Crete. Of interest here is the area directly above the village of Vamvakades (south-east of Kandanos), which can be reached from the latter on a side road. Here, in sparse woodland of *Q. pubescens* there are (UTM: **GE 51.00**):

Barlia robertiana	*Neotinea maculata*
Cephalanthera longifolia	*Ophrys sicula*
Dactylorhiza romana	*Orchis provincialis*
Epipactis microphylla	*Orchis sitiaca*
Limodorum abortivum	

The side road continues further on to Temenia, then runs in an easterly direction to the little village of Rodovani, whence a road runs over basic subsoil to Souyia on the coast. There are many beautiful findspots with huge occurrences of various species along this road; the best is the area barely 1 km from Rodovani (UTM: **GE 50.38**):

Ophrys apifera	*Ophrys sphegodes* ssp. *cretensis*
Ophrys bombyliflora	*Ophrys tenthredinifera*
Ophrys candica	*Orchis collina*
Ophrys fleischmannii	*Orchis fragrans*
Ophrys heldreichii	*Orchis italica*
Ophrys herae	*Orchis lactea*
Ophrys iricolor	*Orchis papilionacea* ssp. *heroica*
Ophrys omegaifera ssp. *basilissa*	*Orchis pauciflora*
Ophrys omegaifera ssp. *omegaifera*	*Orchis simia*
Ophrys phryganea	*Serapias orientalis*
Ophrys sicula	

Peculiarities of the general flora: on the road down to Souyia there are huge populations of *Ebenus cretica*. Shortly before Souyia the road runs past rocky cliffs in which there are a number of leached-out hollows. On the rocks (UTM: **GE 50.55**) the following are to be observed, which flower in the middle of period V:

Campanula laciniata
Verbascum arcturus
Delphinium staphisagria (on the valley floor, under carob trees)

3. Crete – the area around the Omalos High Plateau

Ayia Irini can be reached by driving from the Omalos High Plateau in a south-westerly direction. At the beginning basic rocks predominate, then later acid soils. Directly above Ayia Irini the road emerges from the tree and heather woodland and runs through a little chestnut forest, which has a gulley with water running through it. Some of the water collects in a cement catchment on the roadside. The following can be found here (UTM: **GE 51.64**):

Epipactis microphylla	*Neotinea maculata*
Listera ovata	*Serapias cordigera* ssp. *cretica*

Below the road, in the chestnut forest, there are populations of

Limodorum abortivum	*Cephalanthera longifolia*

The Omalos High Plateau is intensively grazed and itself affords the opportunity to find but few orchids, only on the edges, on the ascent to the surrounding peaks. At the southern end of the plateau is the entrance to the Samaria Gorge; the plethora of species occurring there has been the subject of many publications and will therefore not be mentioned here. Just before the Gorge a path leads off upwards to the east, to the Kallergi Hut; the first part of the ascent passes through species-rich, sparse bushy woodland which mostly consists of *Acer sempervirens*. The area to the north of the Omalos High

Plateau is also of great interest; here the road runs through a little pass. To the north of the latter, in the winding curves of the road, the following are to be found at several places (UTM: **GE 61.38**):

Ophrys candica
Ophrys episcopalis

Orchis quadripunctata

and inside the larger bends in the road (UTM: **GE 61.46**):

Himantoglossum samariense
Ophrys phryganae
Orchis tridentata

Orchis quadripunctata
Neotinea maculata
Arum idaeum

4. Crete – the mountains Bouvala, Siderotas and Xiron

To the south of the main road from Ayia Galini towards Spili there are a number of mountain ridges, partly separated from one another by valleys; these are Bouvala, Siderotas and Xiron, which range between 900 and 1100 metres in height. Plateau-like areas are situated high up in them. There are huge occurrences of many species at numerous locations here, but access to them is relatively difficult. The best way to reach the Bouvala plateau is from Melambes, taking a field path from the upper end of the village, past the school and sports ground, which leads to Saktouria over the mountain plateau (UTM: **KU 88.18**):

Barlia robertiana
Ophrys bombyliflora
Ophrys fusca ssp. creberrima
Ophrys tenthredinifera
Orchis collina
Orchis italica

Orchis lactea
Orchis quadripunctata
Ophrys cinereophila
Ophrys cretica ssp. ariadnae
Ophrys heldreichii
Serapias bergonii

On the ridge of Bouvala near Melambes (CR), 3.4.94

At Vatos, a gravel path can be followed from the middle of the village which leads almost to a plateau situated above the village. Adjoining the lower, meadowy area at a place higher up is an extended area of abandoned terraces, covered with patchy phrygana. Here, on the serpentine rock formations, there are little patches of relatively acid soil, thus it happens that large populations of species typical on such soils are to be found in the immediate vicinity of huge populations of species typical on limestone soils (UTM: **KU 79.44**):

Orchis italica	Orchis sitiaca
Orchis provincialis	Serapias cordigera ssp. cretica
Orchis simia	and many others

The summit of Xiron is best reached from Spili via Mournies, whence a gravel path at the entrance to the village leads up among green serpentine rocks and emerges after a few kilometres (there is a rudimentary signpost pointing "to the coast") onto the road between Drimiskos and Kerames, which indeed leads to the coast. Along this path there are the findspots of the greatest number of species for the whole of Crete (UTM: **KU.79.36/37**):

Anacamptis pyramidalis	Orchis italica
Ophrys candica	Orchis pauciflora
Ophrys cretica ssp. ariadnae	Orchis provincialis
Ophrys episcopalis	Orchis sitiaca
Ophrys heldreichii	Serapias cordigera ssp. cretica
Ophrys mammosa	Serapias lingua
Orchis boryi	Serapias orientalis
Orchis fragrans	Spiranthes spiralis

5. Crete – from Spili to Yerakari

One of the most interesting locations for orchids in Crete lies between Spili and Yerakari, at a location where the road reaches the height of a pass for the first time. This landscape is of small extent but very diversified; many species and suitable biotopes can already be observed from the car. Stony, meadow-covered hills lie to the south of the road, with a gravel road running through them which branches off on the final ascent before Yerakari. Over 40 species are to be found here: (UTM: **KU 79.88/99**):

Aceras anthropophorum	Orchis lactea (very many)
Neotinea maculata	Orchis laxiflora
Ophrys bombyliflora	Orchis pauciflora (masses)
Ophrys candica	Orchis quadripunctata
Ophrys episcopalis	Orchis sitiaca
Ophrys fusca ssp. creberrima	Orchis tridentata
Ophrys fusca ssp. cressa	Serapias bergonii
Ophrys heldreichii	Serapias cordigera ssp. cretica
Orchis boryi (masses)	Serapias lingua
Orchis collina	Spiranthes spiralis
Orchis fragrans	and many others
Orchis italica (masses)	

6. Crete – southern Dikti Mountains

Proceeding from Ierapetra along the main road in a westerly direction for a few kilometres, there is a turn off to the village of Kalamafka, which is surrounded by numerous areas of meadow. Large populations of the following species are to be found there (UTM: **LU. 78.72**):

Anacamptis pyramidalis
Barlia robertiana
Ophrys bombyliflora
Ophrys fleischmannii
Ophrys heldreichii
Ophrys iricolor
Ophrys omegaifera ssp. *omegaifera*
Ophrys phryganae
Ophrys sicula
Ophrys sphegodes ssp. *cretensis*
Ophrys sphegodes ssp. *gortynia*
Ophrys tenthredinifera
Orchis italica
Serapias bergonii

Back on the main road and proceeding in a westerly direction, the village of Kato Simi is reached by turning off to the right just before Pefkos. A gravel track leads from here to the entrance to the largely abandoned village of Epano Simi. Directly at the entrance to it, in a stream bed, the following can be found (UTM: **LU. 67.28**):

Epipactis cretica
Epipactis microphylla

Return in the direction of Kato Simi to the main road, which runs upwards in winding curves into the midst of the peak district of Dikti. It passes through mostly pine forests and touches a ravine with water running through it, mainly overgrown with Acer sempervirens. At a height of about 1350 metres, near the excavation of the Hermaphrodite Temple there, the following can be found in the ravine at the end of May: (UTM: **LU 68.30**):

Anacamptis pyramidalis

Cephalanthera cucullata
Epipactis cretica (abundant)
Limodorum abortivum

Listera ovata (seldom)
Further up, the road passes through

a sparse oak forest, mixed with pines. It ends in a drainless basin (polje) which is intensively grazed (see picture). In the forest above the way leading to it the following can be seen: (UTM:**LU 68.20**):

Barlia robertiana
Cephalanthera cucullata
Himantoglossum samariense
Neotinea maculata
Orchis pauciflora
Orchis prisca
Orchis anatolica
× *Orchis quadripunctata*

Dikti, central Polje (CR), 15.5.01

7. Crete – Thripti high pasture and the Orno mountains

The most well-known findspot in eastern Crete is the Thripti high pasture. It is best reached from Kato Horio, where a rocky gravel road leads away from the church to the high pasture. The way becomes interesting after an altitude of 600 metres, when the lower region of pine forest is reached (UTM: **LU 98.32**):

Ophrys omegaifera ssp. omegaifera
Ophrys sitiaca (March)

Orchis anatolica (relatively typical)
Orchis pauciflora

Further through the forest, in the direction of Thripti, the road crosses several detritus gulleys before it reaches the high pasture. In this area another road turns off to the right, leading to Ayios Yannis. A few hundred metres along the way to the latter there are (UTM: **LU 98.93**):

Orchis anatolica

Orchis prisca

Just before reaching the Thripti high pasture there are clumps of young stone pines, in which Orchis prisca is also to be found. The area of meadows around Thripti contains many interesting orchids, particularly in the areas to the east above the village, and to the west below it (UTM: **LU 98.73/74**):

Ophrys fusca ssp. thriptiensis
Ophrys sitiaca

Orchis laxiflora
Orchis sitiaca (beginning of May)

Alternatively, a gravel path can be taken from Orino in the direction of Thripti; this leads to the high pasture from above, along the northern flank of the mountain ridge, through extensive phrygana. In this area there are: (UTM: **LU 98.84**):

Orchis prisca (abundant)
Orchis pauciflora
Orchis anatolica
× Orchis prisca

Orchis anatolica
× Orchis quadripunctata
Daphne sericea

Similarly, the plateau of the Orno mountains can be reached along a bad gravel track from Orino (UTM: **MU 08.13**):

Ophrys fleischmannii
Ophrys fusca ssp. thriptiensis
Ophrys omegaifera ssp. omegaifera
Ophrys sphegodes ssp. cretensis
Orchis pauciflora
Orchis anatolica
× Orchis quadripunctata
Arum creticum
Daphne sericea (see picture)

Thripti (CR), 3.4.92

8. Karpathos – from Pigadia into the southern part of the island

Directly to the south of Pigadia but unfortunately already threatened by building that is proceeding apace, a narrow asphalt road turns off to the left and leads to a small chapel in a pine forest. In front of the chapel the landscape is very diversified in structure - small meadows alternate with areas of pine woodland (UTM: **NV 12.98**):

Anacamptis pyramidalis
Barlia robertiana
Ophrys bombyliflora
Ophrys cinereophila
Ophrys cretica ssp. ariadnae
Ophrys episcopalis
Ophrys heldreichii
Ophrys omegaifera ssp. omegaifera
Ophrys sicula
Ophrys tenthredinifera
Orchis fragrans
Orchis papilionacea ssp. heroica

Turn back on the main road towards the airport and follow the road which leads off to the right after a few kilometres, towards Menetes. In meadow locations before arriving at Menetes there are (UTM: **NV 12.67**):

Ophrys aegaea
Ophrys cretica ssp. ariadnae
Ophrys episcopalis
Ophrys ferrum-equinum
Ophrys iricolor
Ophrys omegaifera ssp. omegaifera
Ophrys sicula
Orchis anatolica

Shortly after Menetes, on the road to Arkasa, a field track branches off to the right towards Ayios Mamas. In the area where the track branches there are (UTM: **NV 12.36**):

Anacamptis pyramidalis
Ophrys cretica ssp. ariadnae
Ophrys ferrum-equinum
Ophrys heldreichii
Ophrys iricolor (in large number)
Ophrys sicula
Ophrys tenthredinifera
Orchis papilionacea ssp. heroica
Spiranthes spiralis

Before Arkasa, and before it descends towards the coast, the road passes through an extensive area of phrygana. Here, before a small double chapel can be seen on the left hand side, there are (UTM: **NV 12.15**):

Ophrys cretica ssp. ariadnae
Ophrys ferrum-equinum (many)
Ophrys iricolor (many)
Orchis papilionacea ssp. heroica
Spiranthes spiralis

The way back to Pigadia can be taken via Arkasa, Piles and Othos.

9. Karpathos – from Pigadia into the northern part of the island

Follow the road from Pigadia in the direction of Aperi and before arriving there, take the eastern by-pass road in the direction of Kyra Panayia and continue on towards Spoa (gravel track). In the thin clumps of pine there are (UTM: **NV 13.59**):

Barlia robertiana
Neotinea maculata
Ophrys aegaea
Ophrys cinereophila
Ophrys iricolor
Ophrys sicula
Ophrys tenthredinifera
Orchis lactea

After a few kilometres there is an abandoned settlement on the left, below the beach of Apella. The water which emerges above it is collected in a large concrete catchment on the roadside. The extensive area of terraces contains (UTM: **NV 13.29**):

Aceras anthropophorum (masses)
Ophrys aegaea
Ophrys episcopalis
Ophrys ferrum-equinum
Ophrys mammosa

Ophrys sicula
Neotinea maculata
Orchis italica
Orchis laxiflora
Serapias orientalis (masses)

Further in the direction of Spoa there are numerous findspots containing, for example (UTM: **NV 14.31**):

Barlia robertiana
Ophrys aegaea
Ophrys fusca ssp. leucadica
Ophrys iricolor

Ophrys omegaifera ssp. omegaifera
Ophrys sicula
Orchis anatolica
Orchis italica

Coming from Aperi, a little tarmac road leads off to the right before Othos to the Lastos high plateau, which is well worth a visit. A field track leads from there back to Aperi, running about 400 metres above the above-mentioned road to Apella, along the cliff. In addition to many other species, the following are present in large numbers (UTM: **NV. 13.27**):

Orchis anatolica
Orchis laxiflora

Ophrys bombyliflora
Ophrys fusca ssp. leucadica

10. Kasos

This small island consists almost entirely of basic rocks. Practically the whole of the southern part is very arid and extensively over-grazed. It is worthwhile taking the road which leads from the main town of the island, Fre, via Poli to the southern ridge. Before the latter is reached, tracks lead amongst strongly eroded terraces towards the north (UTM: **MV 91.85**):

Ophrys episcopalis
Ophrys heldreichii

Ophrys sicula
Ophrys tenthredinifera

On the ridge amonst stony phrygana there are (UTM: **MV 91.57**):

Ophrys cretica s.l.
Ophrys fusca ssp. leucadica

Orchis anatolica

From here, a track leading further along the ridge turns off in a northeasterly direction into a high pasture area known as Skafi, where there are large populations of *Arum creticum*. In the terraces on the edge of the grazing area, but also before that and not far from the abandoned village, the following may be found (UTM: **MV 91.78**):

Anacamptis pyramidalis
Ophrys sicula
Ophrys cretica

Ophrys tenthredinifera
Ophrys episcopalis
Orchis anatolica

11. Rhodes – from Laerma northwards, towards Apollona

An unmade road runs from Laerma to Apollona, branching to the right in a concrete-clad S-shaped curve at the entrance to the village in the direction of Lardos. It passes through very diversified terrain, often through forest. On hillocks covered with phrygana, along an agricultural track leading off to the right, there are (UTM: **NA 80.74**):

Anacamptis pyramidalis	Ophrys speculum
Ophrys cinereophila	Orchis collina
Ophrys omegaifera	Orchis fragrans
Ophrys sicula	Serapias orientalis

After crossing the Gaidouras by means of a ford with a cement floor there are, on the left of the road, meadows along the river with little patches of woodland where the following may be found (UTM: **NA 80.65**):

Barlia robertiana	Orchis collina
Ophrys cinereophila	Orchis fragrans
Ophrys omegaifera	Orchis sancta
Ophrys sicula	Serapias bergonii

The road proceeds further in the direction of Apollona and comes to a collapsed bridge over the upper reach of the Gaidouras; a new reinforced concrete bridge has been built over it. On the steep, wooded slopes to the left, before the bridge there are (UTM: **NA 80.68**):

Barlia robertiana	Ophrys sitiaca
Ophrys dodekanensis	Orchis anatolica
Ophrys oestrifera	Orchis italica
Ophrys omegaifera	Orchis lactea

After the bridge, there is a field track branching off to the right (UTM: **NA 80.79**):

Ophrys cinereophila	Ophrys sicula
Ophrys dodekanensis	Ophrys sitiaca
Ophrys ferrum-equinum	Ophrys speculum
Ophrys fusca ssp. leucadica	Orchis italica
Ophrys omegaifera	Orchis papilionacea

12. Rhodes – from Laerma towards the south-west, in the direction of Profilia

From Laerma, follow the road in the direction of the Monastery of Thari, but when the road forks take the right fork towards Profilia; the road is unmade. Shortly after the fork, on the right hand side of the road (UTM: **NA 80.20**):

Ophrys fusca ssp. leucadica	Ophrys sicula
Ophrys lucis	Ophrys sitiaca
Ophrys omegaifera	

About one kilometre further along the road towards Profilia, a forest track branching off to the right passes through forest and then enters a very diversified terrain with olive groves, little fields and phrygana, interspersed with small sections of forest (UTM: **NA 80.01**):

Barlia robertiana
Ophrys omegaifera
Ophrys sicula
Ophrys sitiaca

Ophrys speculum
Orchis collina
Orchis fragrans
Anemone coronaria

Return to the road from Laerma to Profilia, which continues mainly through sparse pine woodland, dotted with areas of erosion on which there is almost no vegetation, and dry fields. The following can be found here (UTM: **NV 89.19**):

Ophrys dodekanensis
Ophrys speculum
Orchis anatolica

Orchis collina
Orchis lactea

A little further into the forest there are (UTM: **NV 79.97**):

Ophrys omegaifera

Ophrys sitiaca

Attention: a few kilometres before Profilia the road was blocked by a bridge that had collapsed. This being the case, Profilia can only be reached by crossing a very stony ford – something which can only be accomplished in a Jeep.

13. Rhodes – between Apolakkia, Istrios and Profilia

Take the main road via Gennadio and Vati in the direction of Apolakkia and turn off to the right at Ayia Irini towards Istrios. Before a small, mostly dried-up ford with a cement floor there is a very interesting findspot to the right of the road in a narrow strip of pine forest, which begins about I km before the ford is reached. It is notable not only for its diversity of species, but also for the large numbers of the individual types that are found there (UTM: **NV 79.34**):

Ophrys bombyliflora
Ophrys cinereophila
Ophrys fusca
Ophrys iricolor
Ophrys lucis
Ophrys omegaifera

Ophrys reinholdii
Ophrys regis-ferdinandii
Ophrys sicula
Ophrys speculum
Ophrys tenthredinifera
Orchis papilionacea

The road ascends further to the little mountain village of Istrios, where an unmade track turns off to Ayios Isidoros. About 2.4 kms after this turning, on hills covered with olive groves there are (UTM: **NV 79.67**):

Barlia robertiana
Ophrys candica
Ophrys cinereophila
Ophrys dodekanensis
Ophrys ferrum-equinum
Ophrys iricolor
Ophrys regis-ferdinandii

Ophrys reinholdii
Ophrys sicula
Ophrys speculum
Orchis collina
Orchis fragrans
Orchis lactea
Orchis papilionacea

From here a return to Istrios is recommended, where the turning can be taken for Profilia. On this road there are more interesting findspots, e.g. in the phrygana to the left of the road, about 1.5 kms before Profilia (UTM: **NV 79.96**):

Ophrys regis-ferdinandii	Orchis anatolica
Ophrys reinholdii	Orchis collina
Ophrys sicula	Orchis fragrans
Ophrys speculum	Orchis papilionacea

The main road towards Vati and Gennadio is reached about 3 kms after passing through Profilia.

14. Rhodes - forest paths on the northern edge of Akramitis

The destination for this excusion lies way off the beaten track and is best reached via Laerma and Ayios Isidoros (this part of the way is not asphalted) and from there by following the road to Siana. A good kilometre from the latter village, take the road to the right which runs to the little church at Stellies. From here, a system of fire-prevention tracks, starting with a wide and easily passable main track, connects with the northern face of Akramitis. In the immediate vicinity of the main track, which runs gently uphill through pine woodland, the following may be found. The three findspots mentioned contain only particularly attractive populations, amongst which that of Neotinea maculata is especially abundant (UTM: **NA 60.82**):

Barlia robertiana	Neotinea maculata

(UTM: **NA 60.50**):

Neotinea maculata	Ophrys omegaifera
Ophrys sicula	Orchis anatolica

(UTM: **NA 60.61**):

Neotinea maculata	Ophrys sicula
Ophrys blitopertha	Orchis anatolica
Ophrys cinereophila	Orchis provincialis
Ophrys omegaifera	

In a small forest clearing with cellar-caves and old walls (UTM: **NA 60.61** – approximately: NA 66.870E 01.990N:

Neotinea maculata	Ophrys umbilicata ssp.
Ophrys sicula	umbilicata

On a clearing towards the coast (UTM: **NA 60.92**):

Anacamptis pyramidalis	Orchis anatolica
Barlia robertiana	Orchis fragrans
Neotinea maculata	Orchis sancta
Ophrys reinholdii	Orchis fragrans × Orchis sancta

15. Rhodes – the forest road over Profitis Ilias

Profitis Ilias is reached most easily via Kolimbia, Arhipoli and Eleousa, where the forest road built by the Italians turns off over the mountain (near a sprawling secondary school complex). The road first reaches the little church of Ayios Nikolaos, which belonged to the little village of Fountoukli, now abandoned. Years ago, the immediate area of the latter was a very abundant findspot, but it suffered a considerable loss of the rich diversity of the species there during the 90s (UTM: **NA 81.95**):

Barlia robertiana
Ophrys dodekanensis
Ophrys episcopalis

Ophrys sicula
Ophrys speculum
Orchis italica

Shortly afterwards the very winding and recently asphalted road turns off to the left, down towards Apollona, but follow the old road towards the peak instead. Rich populations of *Paeonia clusii* are conspicuous from the road. The old kilometre marker stones are well suited as a means of orientation for the findspots listed below. However, as the road is very narrow it is not possible to park directly by them, but the car should be left on a forest track nearby. The wider area around the marker stones mentioned should then be examined. Thus at kilometre stone 47 (UTM: **NA 81.23**):

Aceras anthropophorum
Neotinea maculata
Ophrys cinereophila
Ophrys ferrum-equinum
Ophrys lucis
Ophrys oestrifera
Ophrys omegaifera

Ophrys reinholdii
Ophrys sicula
Ophrys umbilicata
Orchis anatolica
Orchis morio
Orchis provincialis (Foto unten)

At kilometre stone 46 (UTM: **NA 81.13**):

Barlia robertiana
Neotinea maculata
Ophrys heldreichii
Ophrys sicula
Ophrys reinholdii
Orchis anatolica
Orchis collina
Orchis italica

Profitis Ilias (RH), 29.3.2002

16. Rhodes – at Kattavia and thereafter towards Mesanagros

Kattavia, the southernmost place on the island, is easily reached along the eastern coast road. At the entrance of the village a gravel road branches off towards Mesanagros. This road can be followed for about 1 km to a water storage cistern on the left and then the vicinity explored (UTM: **NV 67.99**):

Ophrys cretica
Ophrys iricolor
Ophrys fusca ssp. *leucadica*
Ophrys sicula

Ophrys speculum
Ophrys tenthredinifera
Orchis collina
Orchis fragrans

The road further uphill in the direction of Mesanagros passes mostly through dry, phrygana-covered terrain, in which orchids can be sought everywhere, and with success. One possible findspot, for example, is at (UTM: **NV 78.12**):

Ophrys fusca
Ophrys oestrifera
Ophrys tenthredinifera

Orchis collina
Orchis papilionacea
Orchis sancta

Shorty afterwards there is a small chapel on left hand side. The following are found here and in the vicinity (UTM: **NV 78.24**):

Ophrys fusca ssp. *leucadica*
Ophrys iricolor
Ophrys oestrifera
Ophrys reinholdii

Ophrys tenthredinifera
Orchis collina
Orchis papilionacea

A few hundred metres in the direction of Mesanagros (at the height of a small pass):

Ophrys cretica
Ophrys fusca ssp. *leucadica*

Ophrys speculum
Orchis papilionacea

At the turning to Skiadi Monastery (UTM: **NV 78.25**):

Ophrys fusca
Ophrys iricolor

Ophrys omegaifera
Ophrys speculum

The coastal road is reached again via Mesanagros and Lahania.

17. Rhodes – to the south of Kattavia and on the road to Prasonisi

Follow the eastern coastal road in the direction of Kattavia; an area of fields lies to the south of the road, shortly before Kattavia. This can be reached on mostly stony, but also partly grassy tracks, which branch off to the right (southwards) from the coastal road (UTM: **NV 67.98**):

Barlia robertiana
Ophrys fusca ssp. *leucadica*
Ophrys sicula
Ophrys speculum
Ophrys tenthredinifera

Ophrys umbilicata ssp. *umbilicata*
Orchis collina
Serapias orientalis
Serapias parviflora
Spiranthes spiralis and various others

In Kattavia, near two old windmills (one of which has been turned into a house) a recently asphalted road turns off towards the little island of Prasonisi at the southern tip of Rhodes. Follow this road for about 2 kms, roughly to a point below the military camp visible on the right hand side (beware of military manoeuvres!). A search can be instituted in the phrygana on the right hand side, which often appears to be growing in strips (UTM: **NV 67.96-7**):

Anacamptis pyramidalis
Ophrys cinereophila
Ophrys cretica
Ophrys dodekanensis
Ophrys fusca
Ophrys oestrifera
Ophrys omegaifera
Ophrys iricolor

Ophrys umbilicata ssp. *rhodia*
Ophrys sicula
Ophrys speculum
Ophrys tenthredinifera
Orchis collina
Orchis fragrans
Orchis papilionacea
Serapias orientalis

18. Rhodes – the old road from Gennadio to Lahania

On the eastern coastal road in a southwards direction, the old main road branches off about 2 kms beyond Gennadio at an acute angle towards Lahania; considerable stretches of it are only gravelled. It runs through an area of mostly agricultural land with fields, vineyards and olive groves. The sporadic, flat, and arid hills are mostly covered with phrygana, but there are occasional remnants of forest. Several streams with wide, gravel beds cross the terrain from west to east, but there is rarely any water in them. The findspots are listed in order, moving southwards (UTM: **NV 88.14**):

Anacamptis pyramidalis
Ophrys regis-ferdinandii
Ophrys speculum

Orchis collina
Orchis fragrans
Serapias orientalis

(UTM: **NV 80.600E 83.600N**):

Ophrys fusca
Ophrys regis-ferdinandii
Ophrys sicula

Ophrys speculum
Orchis fragrans (masses)

(UTM: **NV 80.600E 83.200N**):

Ophrys speculum
Ophrys regis-ferdinandii

Orchis fragrans (abundant)

(UTM: **NV 80.400E 82.900N** – on a stream bed):

Ophrys sicula
Orchis collina

Ophrys speculum
Serapias orientalis

(UTM: **NV 80.400E 83.300N** – a forested curve in the road):

Ophrys tenthredinifera

After reaching Lahania, take the short connecting road to the coastal road. The following may be found here in the vicinity of the signpost marking the beginning of the village (UTM: **NV 78.80**):

Ophrys sicula
Ophrys speculum
Ophrys tenthredinifera

Orchis collina
Orchis papilionacea
Serapias bergonii

19. Rhodes – coastal phrygana near Plimiri

Take the coastal road in a southerly direction via Gennadio, until a turn-off signposted to Plimiri Beach is reached. Do not take this turning, but take an agricultural track which runs off to the left, about 1 km further south and near the village of Hohlakas, towards the coast. This leads through hilly terrain with small fields; the hills are partly covered with phrygana and remnants of forest. This terrrain extends down to the coast. The following list of findspots constitutes only a selection (UTM: **NV 77.57**):

Anacamptis pyramidalis
Limodorum abortivum
Ophrys cinereophila
Ophrys cretica
Ophrys ferrum-equinum
Ophrys iricolor
Ophrys oestrifera
Ophrys omegaifera

Ophrys regis-ferdinandii
Ophrys sicula
Ophrys speculum
Ophrys tenthredinifera
Orchis collina
Orchis fragrans
Orchis papilionacea
Spiranthes spiralis

(UTM: **NV 77.56**):

Anacamptis pyramidalis
Ophrys cinereophila
Ophrys cretica
Ophrys fusca
Ophrys omegaifera
Ophrys regis-ferdinandii

Ophrys sicula
Ophrys speculum
Ophrys tenthredinifera
Orchis fragrans
Orchis papilionacea
Serapias orientalis

(UTM: **NV 77.65**):

Ophrys cinereophila
Ophrys oestrifera
Ophrys regis-ferdinandii
Ophrys speculum

Ophrys tenthredinifera
Orchis fragrans
Orchis papilionacea
Serapias orientalis

(UTM: **NV 77.76**):

Anacamptis pyramidalis
Ophrys regis-ferdinandii
Ophrys sicula
Ophrys speculum
Orchis fragrans

Orchis collina
Orchis papilionacea
Serapias orientalis
Serapias parviflora
Spiranthes spiralis

Coastal phrygana near Plimiri (RH), 17.3.02

235

20. Rhodes – the road from Laerma to Ayios Isidoros

Take the gravel track which begins in Laerma and proceed toward Ayios Isidoros; a little way behind the village there is a charcoal works. A little further on, to the left of the road, on wooded slopes, in places dripping with water, there are (UTM: **NA 80.32**):

Ophrys dodekanensis
Ophrys omegaifera

Ophrys mammosa
Ophrys reinholdii

2 kms further on, along a field track branching off to the west, there are (UTM: **NA 80.14**):

Ophrys oestrifera
Ophrys sicula

Orchis fragrans
Orchis sancta

Back again on the main road, which snakes upwards in hairpin bends to a foothill of Attaviros, then follows its backbone for about 2 kms and subsequently leads down into a flat valley, on the northern side of which Ayios Isidoros is situated. On this downhill stretch, at a left-hand bend in the pine forest (UTM: **NA 70.93**):

Anacamptis pyramidalis
Barlia robertiana
Cephalanthera epipactoides
Ophrys cinereophila

Ophrys omegaifera
Ophrys phryganae
Orchis anatolica
Orchis italica

On reaching the floor of the valley, turn left into a system of narrow field paths which connect the hilly terrain opposite the village of Ayios Isidoros with small vineyards, olive groves and pine woods (UTM: **NA 70.82 – 70.93**):

Barlia robertiana
Ophrys blitopertha
Ophrys cinereophila
Ophrys episcopalis
Ophrys ferrum-equinum
Ophrys fusca
Ophrys lucis
Ophrys mammosa
Ophrys oestrifera
Ophrys omegaifera
Ophrys phryganae

Ophrys regis-ferdinandii
Ophrys reinholdii
Ophrys rhodia
Ophrys sicula
Ophrys speculum
Orchis anatolica (masses)
Orchis collina
Orchis italica
Orchis papilionacea
Serapias bergonii

Literature cited

BATEMAN, R. M., PRIDGEON,A.M., & CHASE,M.W. (1997): Phylogenetics of subtribe Orchidinae (Orchidoideae, Orchidaceae) based on nuclear ITS sequences. 2. Infrageneric relationships and reclassification to achieve monophyly of *Orchis sensu stricto*. - Lindleyana **12**(3): 113-141.

BATEMAN, R.M. (2001): Evolution and classification of European orchids: insights from molecular and morphological characters. - Jour. Eur. Orch. 33(1): 33-119.

BRUMMITT, R.K. & POWELL, C.E. (1992): Authors of plant names. - Kew.

CREUTZBURG, N. (1966): DIE SÜDÄGAISCHE INSELKETTE. BAU UND GEOLOGISCHE VERGANGENHEIT. - ERDKUNDE 20: 20-30.

FLEISCHMANN, H. (1925): Beitrag zur Orchideenflora der Insel Kreta. - Oesterr. Bot. Z. 74(7-9): 180-194.

GÖLZ, P., REINHARD, H.R., ALIBERTIS, C., ALIBERTIS, A., GACK, C. & PAULUS, H.F. (1996): Gestaltwandel innerhalb kretischer Orchideenaggregate im Verlauf der Monate Januar bis Mai. - Jour. Eur. Orch. 28(4): 641-701.

JAHN, R. & SCHÖNFELDER, P. (1995): Exkursionsflora für Kreta. - Stuttgart.

IGME (ed.) (1984): Geological map of Greece 1:50.000, Kassos Island. - Bureau de Publication des Cartes Géologiques de l' I.G..M.E. (Institute of Geology and Mineral Exploration).

KALTEISEN, M. & E. WILLING (1981): Verbreitungskarten der Orchideen von Rhodos. - Mitt.Bl. Arbeitskrs. Heim. Orchid. Baden-Württemberg **19**(4): 853-865.

KRETZSCHMAR, G. & KRETZSCHMAR, H. (1996) Orchideen der Insel Naxos. - Ber. Arbeitskr. Heim. Orch. 13(1): 4-30.

KRETZSCHMAR, G., KRETZSCHMAR, H. & ECCARIUS, W. (2001): Orchideen auf Rhodos. - Bad Hersfeld.

KRETZSCHMAR, G., KRETZSCHMAR, H. & ECCARIUS, W. (2002): Orchideen auf Kreta, Kasos, Karpathos. - Bad Hersfeld.

KRETZSCHMAR, H., D. WENKER & E. WILLING (1984): Orchideenkartierung der Insel Rhodos - aktuelle Übersicht. - Ber. Arbeitskrs. Heim. Orchid. **1**(2): 130-146.

MUTTI, E., G. OROMBELLI & R. POZZI (1960-1965): Geological map of Rhodes Island (Greece).

PAULUS, H.F. (1998): Der Ophrys fusca s.str. - Komplex auf Kreta und anderer Ägäisinseln mit Beschreibungen von O. blitopertha, O. creberrima, O. cinereophila, O. cressa, O. thriptiensis, und O. creticola spp. nov. (Orchidaceae) - Jour. Eur. Orch. 30(1): 157-201.

PAULUS,H.F.(2001):Daten zur Bestäubungsbiologie und Systematik der Gattung Ophrys in Rhodos (Griechenland) mit Beschreibung von Ophrys parvula, Ophrys persephonae, Ophrys lindia, Ophrys eptapigiensis spec. nov. aus der Ophrys fusca s.str. Gruppe und Ophrys cornutula spec. nov. aus der Ophrys oestrifera-Gruppe (Orchidaceae und Insecta, Apoidea). - Ber. Arbeitskr. Heim. Orch. 18(1): 38-86.

RAUS, T. (1991): Asia or Europe - The phytogeographical position of the Karpathos archipelago (SE Aegean, Greece). - Flora Vegetatio Mundi IX: 301-310.

Further Literature

BUTTLER, K. P. (1986): Orchideen. Die wildwachsenden Arten und Unterarten Europas, Vorderasiens und Nordafrikas. - München.

DELFORGE, P. (2001): Guide des Orchideés d'Europe d'Afrique du Nord et du Proche-Orient. 2.Ed.- Lausanne, Paris.

JAHN, R. & SCHÖNFELDER, P. (1995): Exkursionsflora für Kreta. - Stuttgart.

KRETZSCHMAR, G., KRETZSCHMAR, H. & ECCARIUS, W. (2001): Orchideen auf Rhodos. - Bad Hersfeld.

KRETZSCHMAR, G., KRETZSCHMAR, H. & ECCARIUS, W. (2002): Orchideen auf Kreta, Kasos, Karpathos. - Bad Hersfeld.

RECHINGER, K.H. (1943): Flora Aegaee. - Denkschr. Akad. Wiss. Wien 105: 1-924.

RECHINGER, K.H. (1949): Florae Aegaeae supplementum. - Phyton (Horn) 1(2-4): 194-228.

Overview of the Taxa according to region

70 species with 23 subspecies, occurrence of 5 instable or questionable species

(**KR (1)** = Crete, **KP (2)**= Karpathos, **KA (3)** = Kasos, **RH (4)** = Rhodes)

1	2	3	4		Page
*	*	*	*	*Aceras anthropophorum* (L.) W.T. AITON	18
*	*	*	*	*Anacamptis pyramidalis* (L.) RICH.	20
*	*	*	*	*Barlia robertiana* (LOISEL.) GREUTER	22
*				*Cephalanthera cucullata* BOISS.& HELDR. ex RCHB. f	24
*				*Cephalanthera damasonium* (MILL.) DRUCE	196
		*		*Cephalanthera epipactoides* FISCH. & C.A. MEY	26
*		*		*Cephalanthera longifolia* (L.) FRITSCH	28
*				*Cephalanthera rubra* (L.) RICH.	196
		*		*Comperia comperiana* K. KOCH	30
*		*		*Dactylorhiza romana* (SEBAST.) SOÓ	32
*				*Epipactis cretica* KALOP. & ROBATSCH	34
*				*Epipactis microphylla* (EHRH.) SW.	36
*				*Epipogium aphyllum* SW.	196
*				*Himantoglossum samariense* C. & A. ALIBERTIS	38
*		*	*	*Limodorum abortivum* (L.) SW.	40
*				*Listera ovata* L.	42
*		*	*	*Neotinea maculata* (DESF.) STEARN	44
	*	*		*Ophrys aegaea* KALTEISEN & H.R. REINHARD	46
*		*	*	*Ophrys apifera* HUDS.	48
*		*	*	*Ophrys bombyliflora* LINK	50
				Ophrys cretica (VIERH.) E. NELSON	52
*	*	*		ssp. *ariadnae* (PAULUS) H. KRETZSCHMAR	52
		*		ssp. *beloniae* H. & G. KRETZSCHMAR	54
*				ssp. *bicornuta* H. KRETZSCHMAR & R. JAHN	56
*				ssp. *cretica*	58
				Ophrys episcopalis-oestrifera - Group	60
*	*		*	*Ophrys candica* GREUTER, MATTHÄS & RISSE	62
		*		*Ophrys dodekanensis* H.KRETZSCHMAR & C.A.J. KREUTZ	64
*	*	*	*	*Ophrys episcopalis* POIR.	66
*	*	*	*	*Ophrys heldreichii* SCHLTR.	68
		*		*Ophrys oestrifera* M. BIEB.	70
	*	*		*Ophrys ferrum-equinum* DESF.	72
				Ophrys fusca - Group	74
		*		*Ophrys attaviria* D. RÜCKBRODT & WENKER	76
		*		*Ophrys blithopertha* PAULUS & GACK	78
*	*	*	*	*Ophrys cinereophila* PAULUS & GACK	80
*				*Ophrys fleischmannii* HAYEK	82
				Ophrys fusca LINK	84
*				ssp. *creberrima* (PAULUS) H. KRETZSCHMAR	84
*				ssp. *cressa* (PAULUS) H. KRETZSCHMAR	86
*				ssp. *creticola* (PAULUS) H. KRETZSCHMAR	88
	*	*	*	ssp. *leucadica* (RENZ) H. KRETZSCHMAR	90
*				ssp. *thriptiensis* (PAULUS) H. KRETZSCHMAR	92
*		*	*	*Ophrys iricolor* DESF.	94
*				*Ophrys mesaritica* PAULUS & C. & A. ALIBERTIS	96
				Ophrys omegaifera H. FLEISCHM.	98
*				ssp. *basilissa* (C. & A. ALIBERTIS & H.R. REINHARD) H. KRETZSCHMAR	98
*		*	*	ssp. *omegaifera*	100
*		*		*Ophrys sitiaca* PAULUS & C. & A. ALIBERTIS	102
		*		*Ophrys lucis (*KALTEISEN & H.R. REINHARD) PAULUS	104

Acknowledgements

Grateful thanks to the following who have contributed to this book with photographic material:

H. BAUMGARTNER (Kehl)
H. BAUMANN (Böblingen)
H. BLATT (Friedberg)
S. HERTEL (Haag)

R. KOHLMÜLLER (Erlangen)
C. KREUTZ (Landgraaf, Niederlande)
W. KREY (Neumünster)
W. LÜDERS (Herzberg)